hand and machine woodwork

REVISED EDITION

H.G. MILLER
Technical Director
General Brock High School
Burlington, Ontario

illustrated by
G. FANTUZ, KEITH KING, *and* KEITH MILLER

THE MACMILLAN COMPANY OF CANADA LIMITED TORONTO

ISBN 0-7705-0951-7

Cover photographs courtesy of the following:

Furniture and Furnishings: top left, centre, bottom left, bottom centre;
Ontario Ministry of Industry and Tourism: top centre, top right;
Sklar Furniture Limited: lower right.

Printed in Canada

editor's preface

The texts that make up this series are designed for use by students who are making a serious effort to master the fundamental theory and practice of the technological subjects taught in the secondary schools. Since students enrolled in these courses are also required to study mathematics, the sciences, and the humanities, many doors are open to them upon graduation.

Because of this fact, strong emphasis should be placed on problem-solving and the technological aspects of each subject. To know *why* is often more important that to know *how*. It is hoped that the assignment questions and problems included will serve as a starting point in this regard.

A glossary of terms peculiar to each subject is included in most of the texts. Students frequently fail to understand what is taught in a lesson because the precise meanings of words and terms new to them are not clearly understood.

Short drills and tests based on the meaning of words peculiar to the subject will ensure an improvement in learning.

It is hardly necessary to point out the shortcomings of a course that depends on a single textbook. Teachers are urged to have their students make liberal use of other texts and reference books.

The authors, each of whom spent many years in industry or, the trades before entering the teaching profession, have no desire to limit the creative talents of teachers or students. As far as projects are concerned, where these are included, they are merely suggestive in nature and are designed as a starting point from which the teacher can develop others suited to the individual needs of his students. A variety of projects handled in this way can serve as a strong motivating force.

author's preface

This book was written with the hope that it would create a greater interest in woodworking and greater appreciation for fine workmanship. It is specifically intended as an aid for students who are beginning the study of woodwork and require an introduction to the tools, machine operations, and safety precautions involved. The topics covered are based on recognized course of study outlines for this subject. They have, however, been enlarged and new topics added to present woodworking as an enjoyable hobby or as the basis for an occupation.

In the revision the book has been updated, some chapters have been combined, and three new chapters have been added, with approximately fifty new drawings and photographs. The new material includes a chapter on portable electric hand tools — the various types, instructions on how to use them, and safety precautions; a chapter on laminating and bending, listing the advantages of laminated curved members, methods of clamping, the use of caul blocks and presses, and steam bending; and a chapter on cabinet and furniture details, which are so necessary in the designing and building of modern furniture and cabinets. Such details as frames, gables, shelves, drawers, doors, hardware, and wood joints are described and illustrated. The book has been completely reset in a new format, with the use of a second colour to clarify some of the diagrams, and the addition of colour photographs of some of the commoner woods on the endpapers.

Hand and Machine Woodwork should only be considered as an introduction to the subject. For further study many good reference books are available, some of which are mentioned in the Bibliography. To keep up to date on the most recent developments students should take advantage of some of the better current trade magazines, which describe and illustrate new materials and techniques.

It would be difficult to prepare a book of this nature for publication without the co-operation and assistance of many individuals and firms. The author, therefore, wishes to acknowledge and thank the following people: the general editor, Professor Alan Frizzell, who acted as adviser and was instrumental in initiating this series of shop texts; Mr. Keith Steven, who provided valuable editorial assistance in preparing the manuscript for the revised edition; the many critics who read the initial manuscript and made valuable suggestions; the manufacturers who supplied many of the photographs; the editorial staff of the Macmillan Company of Canada; and my wife Dorothy, who gave me continued encouragement, as well as doing all of the typing.

H.G. Miller

contents

hand and machine woodwork

introduction

Woodworking can be as interesting to study as it is enjoyable and relaxing to work at. It is an activity that involves the combined use of the mind and the hands for the creation of something worth while. The project undertaken may be a large and involved one, requiring many hand tools, power machines, and materials, or a small, simple one made from materials and tools at hand.

Woodworking is many things to many people. To some it is a hobby that provides relaxation and change from their usual daily activities; to others it is a useful and economical means of maintaining and repairing their own homes or cottages. Some who become quite proficient build or remodel their homes, an accomplishment that affords them a great deal of satisfaction as well as a saving of money. For still others, woodworking forms the basis of their occupation.

The study of woodwork is offered as a general subject in the school curriculum as part of a basic education and is aimed at providing students with a manual skill, regardless of their future occupation. For many students, however, this may kindle an interest in the subject and a desire for further training, which can lead, in turn, to an interesting and rewarding career in some branch of the building industry. Woodworking courses also provide an excellent grounding for studies beyond the secondary school level. Students entering such fields as engineering, architecture, art, furniture design and interior design at colleges and universities will find that they benefit from having taken woodwork in high school.

It helps if you begin the study of woodwork with the realization that it is a subject that will be of value to you in many ways, and one most people enjoy. Do your best in each project you undertake; the better you do anything the more you will enjoy doing it. Do not give up if the job does not turn out as well as you had hoped; perfection in woodworking comes only with practice. Each well-made project will add to your skill and confidence.

Although we do live in a machine age, when machines perform most manufacturing operations, including those involved with products made from wood, there are still many advantages to being proficient in a hand skill such as woodworking. Hand skills are still fundamental to the woodworking and building industry. Once such a skill is acquired it will remain with you as a valuable accomplishment. It develops an appreciation for the good work of others and a sense of pride in your own. The planning and reading of woodworking drawings promote clear and logical thinking, and the layout, cutting, and assembling of a project develop a high standard of accuracy, precision, and neatness. Working with your hands can also be good for your physical and mental well-being because it is generally enjoyable and relaxing. Building things with wood and hand tools also requires planning and offers great scope for creative design.

Wood as a structural material is one of the most satisfactory media in which to express oneself, for it is a living substance with warmth, texture, and beauty. Although many materials are used as a substitute, none has the same

1

qualities as wood. On the other hand, metal and plastics may be employed effectively in combination with wood for some projects.

With the growth of our country and the advance in building, the skills of the woodworker have found an ever-widening field in all branches of construction. Building construction, with all of its related trades, is our largest industry, and woodworking is one of the most important parts of that industry.

In the past there has been a shortage of craftsmen skilled in furniture making and design, and this gap has been filled largely by imported labour. With our increase in population there has been a corresponding rise in the demand for trained carpenters and cabinetmakers.

Some of the possible occupational goals in woodworking and its related fields are:

(a) To enter the construction industry as an apprentice with the aim of becoming a journeyman carpenter for work on residential, commercial, or industrial buildings.

(b) To work for a large construction firm in a supervisory role as foreman, layout man, estimator, or construction superintendent. People who are capable of filling these positions are in great demand. They are usually graduates of a high school, junior college, or technological institute, who have a good background in mathematics and English as well as a specialized technical training.

(c) To become a speculative home-builder. A large percentage of our homes are produced by builders who purchase land and construct homes on it, and then sell them to prospective home-owners. This is one method of entering the building business for yourself after you have gained experience working for others.

(d) To become a general contractor. This is another method of owning and managing your own business. These persons engage in commercial, industrial, and residential construction, generally on a contract basis. Often the general contractor is a skilled carpenter who hires and supervises other buildings tradesmen such as bricklayers, plumbers, and electricians, as they are required.

(The following are some of the possibilities in branches of the woodworking industry not directly connected with the building industry.)

(e) To work as a cabinetmaker in a furniture factory or in a custom shop that specializes in furniture, store fixtures, or commercial display work.

(f) To become a pattern maker. The highly skilled tradesmen in this branch make wooden patterns for parts that are to be cast in metal. The patterns are set into damp sand and then removed to form a mould. The hollow left in the sand when the pattern is taken out becomes a receptacle of the correct shape and size into which molten metal can be poured to produce the desired metal part, which is called a casting. The pattern maker plays an important role in modern industrial development.

(g) To find employment in the boat-building industry. This is a specialized branch of woodworking that offers growing opportunities for an interesting future. While steel, plastic, and fibreglass are also used for boats, none is able to reproduce the fine lines and excellent qualities of a wooden hull.

There is a bright future in woodworking, especially in building construction, for anyone who is interested in it and who is willing to prepare himself for the opportunities that are available. In a large country such as ours with a fast-expanding building program it is obvious that the possibilities for those who are skilled in the use of wood and other types of building materials will increase for many years to come.

All the tradesmen referred to above, although employed in different branches of the woodworking industry, use the same basic materials, tools, and machines. The same skills and knowledge of general woodworking are fundamental to all of them. It is this general information that is covered in this book.

ASSIGNMENT

1. List the various branches of the woodworking industry.

2. State two occupational possibilities in building construction for a well-trained woodworker.

3. What factors do all branches of the woodworking industry have in common?

4. In what practical way would the study of woodwork be of value to anyone who does not intend to make any branch of the woodworking industry his life work?

5. List some of the advantages of acquiring a hand skill.

6. In which academic subjects should a person have a good general knowledge, if he wishes to hold a responsible position in the building construction industry?

7. State any special interest or appeal that the study of woodwork and working with tools and machines have for you.

CHAPTER TWO

shop safety

Modern tools and power machines can save you a great deal of time if you learn how to use them safely and correctly. Safety is an aspect of woodworking that cannot be overstressed. The moving parts and sharp knives or cutting edges become a serious hazard if the equipment is not properly used. Many of the machines require special safety precautions, and these are described in later chapters. Listed here are the general safety rules to be followed in any shop.

1. The best precaution is to be safety-minded at all times. Be aware of the hazards in the shop and be willing to take proper safety precautions. There is no point in learning safety rules unless you are willing to take them seriously. Safety must become a habit.

2. Promote safety in the shop by conducting yourself in a workmanlike manner, and by treating tools and machines with respect, and your fellow workers as yourself. Take the subject seriously, and realize that woodwork is an important part of your education. "A good worker is a safe worker."

3. Dress safely. Do not wear a jacket or a loose sweater. Shirt sleeves should be rolled up. If you are wearing a tie, remove it or tuck it in before starting to work. A shop apron should be worn to protect your clothing. Always wear safety glasses when operating or standing near any type of woodworking machinery.

4. Never operate machines until you have been given full instructions on their use. Whether or not you are permitted to operate machines may well depend on your knowledge of the equipment and your general attitude toward safety.

5. Do not use machines until all the guards are in place.

6. Be neat. Keep your bench and working area clear of unnecessary material such as scrap wood, especially wood with projecting nails. Always keep your tools and supplies in order.

7. Be careful when carrying sharp-edged tools such as chisels. Keep the edges pointing down so as not to injure others. Never carry such tools in your pocket.

8. All injuries, no matter how slight, should be reported immediately to the instructor for first-aid treatment. Remember that any unattended injury might become seriously infected.

9. Pay strict attention to what you are doing. Do not carry on a conversation with anyone while you are operating a machine; a power woodworking machine demands your undivided attention.

10. Place all paint or oily rags in closed metal containers.

11. Be ready and willing to co-operate and assist other students at al times. Many accidents have resulted when one person has at-

James C. Fish Photography

Fig. 2:1   Student Properly Dressed for Work

tempted to perform an operation that required the assistance of a second person.

12. Acquire safety habits. Perform all operations the safe way. Remember, eyes and fingers can never be replaced.

Safety is strongly stressed in industry. Most companies conduct safety campaigns in an effort to prevent accidents, which are costly both to employees and to the company. They are assisted in these programs by many private and government-sponsored organizations and associations actively involved in industrial safety. The most important of these is the Industrial Accident Prevention Association, which, together with its affiliated branches dealing with specific areas such as construction, chemical, and highway accident prevention and the Workmen's Compensation Board, campaigns

5

vigorously through training programs and publicity to promote safer working conditions in all branches of industry and to encourage the safety habits and attitudes of all industrial workers.

We are all expected to adhere to safety rules throughout our lives in such matters as driving, or working in a shop, in a factory, or on a construction site, or in any other form of industrial activity. Likewise, for your own safety in the school shop, you will be expected to observe the foregoing list of general shop safety rules. You are asked to accept them not as arbitrary restrictions but rather as a part of a constructive program for your own benefit and safety. You will be a better worker if you adopt a mature attitude toward safety rules.

ASSIGNMENT

1. Why should "Safety First" be stressed in woodworking?

2. Good general shop conduct is an aid in preventing accidents. Why is this so?

3. How should you be dressed for shop work?

4. Why is neatness a factor in shop safety?

5. Why should even slight injuries receive first aid?

6. List any safety precautions other than those given here that you consider should be observed in a woodworking shop.

7. Why are industries very concerned about maintaining a good safety record?

8. What should your attitude be regarding safety in the school woodworking shop?

Research Assignment

9. Design an original safety poster that could be displayed on the shop bulletin board. You may wish to study some of the safety bulletins issued by the Industrial Accident Prevention Association for ideas and inspiration, but do not copy one of these.

CHAPTER THREE

measuring and layout tools

To make anything worth-while of wood or of any other material requires accurate measuring and layout with hand tools. It is important that you develop the skill necessary to make precision layouts. You will then be able to make each piece of wood the correct shape and size to fit properly together with others to make a complete and attractive project.

Although it is probable that Canada and the United States will change to the metric system at some future date, the basic unit of measurement used in woodwork is still the *foot*. The foot is divided into twelve inches, and each inch, in turn, is broken into fractions such as ½, ¼, ⅛, ¹/₁₆, and ¹/₃₂. (On some rules the inch is divided into tenths or into twelfths.) Most general woodwork does not require fractions smaller than ¹/₃₂. Whether the dimensions are for a building or for a small piece of furniture, the units of measurement are the same, and you should be thoroughly familiar with inch fractions to enable you to read a rule accurately and quickly. This is a *must* for all types of practical work.

Figure 3:1 shows an enlarged view of the inch and fraction graduations. Make sure you know and understand them.

The abbreviation for a foot is a short stroke above and to the right of a number. Thus 6' indicates 6 feet. A double stroke above and to the right of a number indicates inches; hence 6" represents 6 inches. The figures 8' 7½" indicate 8 feet 7½ inches.

Always express a fraction in its lowest denominator. For example ¹²/₁₆ "

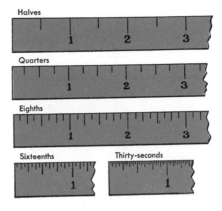

Fig. 3:1   Inch Graduations

should be expressed as ¾", and ¹⁶/₃₂ " as ½".

Measuring tools

The size of the measuring tool that a woodworker should use will depend on the type of work he is doing. To measure the foundation of a house he might use a 50' or 100' tape. If he were making a footstool, he would use a folding rule or a 12" metal scale. (Metal rules 6" or 12" long are referred to as *scales*. They are often marked off in thirty-seconds or sixty-fourths of an inch.) Some of the many types of rules used by woodworkers for various purposes are shown in Figures 3:2 to 3:6.

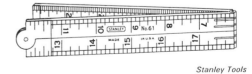

Stanley Tools

Fig. 3:2   2' Folding Rule

Stanley Tools

Fig. 3:3   6' Zigzag Rule

Stanley Tools

Fig. 3:4   6' Steel Tape

Stanley Tools

Fig. 3:5   50' Steel Tape

Stanley Tools

Fig. 3:6   Caliper Rule

Although each of these measuring tools is used for a special purpose, all are marked off in graduations equal to the standard fractions used in linear measure.

The steel pocket tape can be very useful in making inside measurements, as shown in Figure 3:7.

The degree of accuracy with which we use a rule will depend on the purpose of the measurement. If the rule is being used only to determine the dimensions of a piece of rough stock or to cut a piece of stock to a rough length, not quite as much care needs to be taken as when a final layout for a finished part is being made, where precision measuring is required. There are definite procedures that are generally followed when making final layout operations:

1. *Measure to length.* Before measuring a piece of stock to the correct length, one end should be squared and the layout started from there. With a try square and a sharp pencil or a knife, mark a line all the way around the stock about ½" in from the end. With a back saw cut along this line.

Place the rule on edge, with the number indicating the desired length exactly over the squared end of the piece. With a sharp pencil, make a mark at the end of the rule, as shown in Figure 3:8. Another method is to place the end of the rule at the squared end of the stock and make a mark opposite the required length on the rule, as in Figure 3:9.

2. *Measure to width.* When marking a piece of stock to the correct width, place the end of the rule on the face edge of the stock and mark at the desired width, as shown in Figure 3:10. A marking gauge (described on page 13) may also be used for this operation.

If a piece of stock is to be divided into several equal widths, it may be

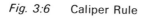

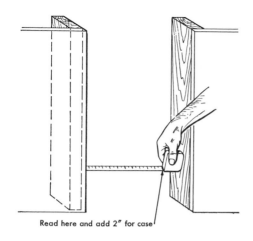

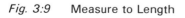
Read here and add 2" for case

Fig. 3:7   Inside Measurement

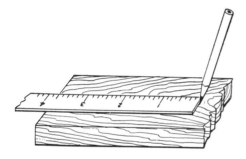

Fig. 3:8   Measure to Length

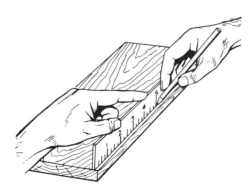

Fig. 3:9   Measure to Length

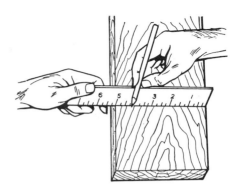

Fig. 3:10   Measure to Width

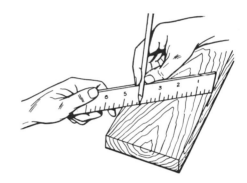

Fig. 3:11   A Convenient Method of Dividing a Piece of Stock into Five Equal Parts

easier to place the rule across the board diagonally so that the divisions can be marked off from the whole numbers, as shown in Figure 3:11.

Layout tools

There are several hand tools generally used for layout purposes:

Try square

The try square is a small, accurately made tool consisting of a wood or metal handle with a steel blade generally 6" long. The handle and the blade form a fixed 90° angle. This makes it an excellent tool for laying out and checking right angles. It is also used as a testing

9

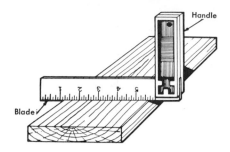
Handle

Blade

Fig 3:12   A Try Square Used to Test a Piece of Stock for Flatness

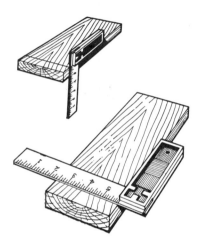

Fig. 3:13   Squaring a Line on the Face and the Edge of a Piece of Stock

Fig. 3:14   Hold the pencil at a slight outward angle for an accurate layout.

tool as shown in Figure 3:12, or as a rule or a straightedge.

For making any layout with a square, a rule, or a straightedge, the lines should be distinct and drawn or scribed as close as possible to the edge of the tool being used. If a pencil is used, it should be sharp and held at a slight outward angle for an accurate layout (see Figure 3:14).

For a very accurate layout a knife can be used instead of a pencil. A knife will make a fine scored line in the surface of the wood, much narrower than a pencil line. The scored cut should be directly against the edge of the layout tool, as shown in Figure 3:15.

Fig. 3:15   Using a Knife for a Very Accurate Layout

Combination square

The combination square is useful for several purposes. It has a movable head that can be clamped to the blade at any position, thus enabling it to be used as a marking gauge. The head has two faces, one machined at 45° and the other at 90°, so that either a mitred (45°) layout or a right-angle (90°) layout may be made with it. Most combination squares are provided with a spirit level for levelling and plumbing (checking work to see that it is in an upright position). A scriber is also provided for more accurate layout. Some of the uses of the combination square are shown in Figure 3:18.

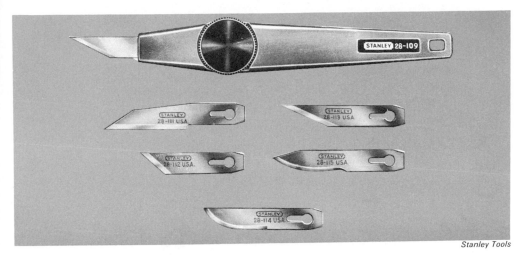

Stanley Tools

Fig. 3:16   Layout and Marking Knife

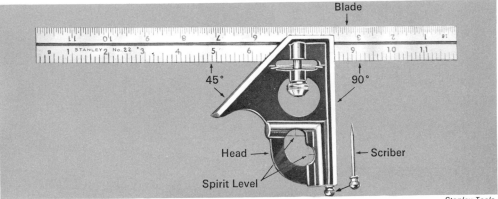

Stanley Tools

Fig. 3:17   Combination Square

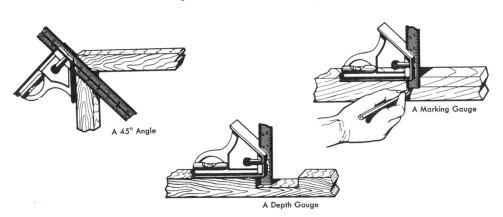

Fig. 3:18   Uses of the Combination Square

Sliding T-bevel

The sliding T-bevel has an adjustable blade that can be clamped to the handle at any desired angle. These tools are made in several sizes and may have either wooden or metal handles.

The sliding T-bevel is useful for laying out any angle cut, as the bevel may be set to various angles with the aid of triangles, a framing square, or a protractor, as shown in Figure 3:20.

To set the sliding T-bevel to a given angle with a framing square, these figures may be used:

For a 60° angle use 12″ and 20⅞″

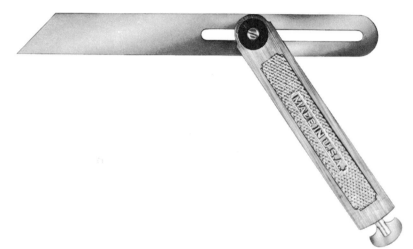

Stanley Tools

Fig. 3:19   Sliding T-Bevel

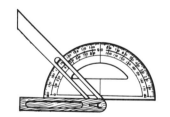

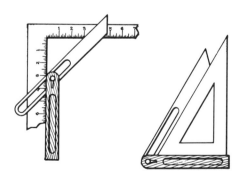

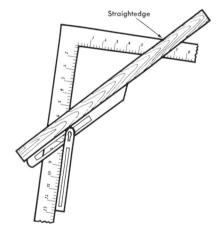

Straightedge

Fig. 3:20   Setting the Sliding T-Bevel to an Angle

Fig. 3:21   Using a Straightedge with a Framing Square to Set the T-Bevel to an Angle

For a 45° angle use 12" and 12"
For a 30° angle use 12" and 6 $^{15}/_{16}$ "
For a 20° angle use 12" and 4⅜"
For a 10° angle use 12" and 2⅛"

Since the blade of the T-bevel is not long enough to reach diagonally across the square between these numbers, a straightedge can be used and the T-bevel blade set to it.

Marking gauge

The marking gauge is a tool used for the accurate scribing of lines parallel to a planed edge or face. It is generally made from a light, though tough, wood. It has a sliding head that can be tightened on the beam at any desired position by a thumbscrew. The beam is graduated into inches and sixteenths to a length of six inches. A steel marking-pin is mounted through the beam at the start of the measuring scale. The face plate and the shoe protect the head and the beam from excessive wear. The pin may become bent or pushed off the first graduation mark, and it is therefore advisable to measure the distance between the pin and the face plate, as shown in Figure 3:23.

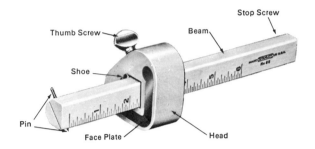

Stanley Tools

Fig. 3:22 Marking Gauge

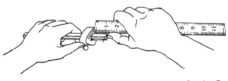

Stanley Tools

Fig. 3:23 Setting the Marking Gauge

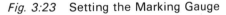

Mortise gauge

The mortise gauge is similar to the marking gauge with the exception that it has two pins and two beams instead of one. It is used for laying out mortise-and-tenon joints where double layout lines are required. The newer mortise gauge, such as the one shown in Figure 3:25, is an all-metal tool.

Stanley Tools

Fig. 3:24 Scribing Stock to Thickness

Fig. 3:25 Mortise Gauge

An all-purpose layout and testing tool can be used for several operations and as a substitute for such tools as a square, a level, a marking gauge, a protractor, a depth gauge, a beam compass, as well as a screw, dowel, and nail gauge. This tool is shown in Figure 3:26. A tool used for bisecting angles is shown in Figure 3:27.

Tools for curved layouts

Many tools are available for making circles and arcs, and there has been some confusion about the names of these tools. There is the standard *compass* that you have probably often used for drawing circles. *Scribers* are a similar tool made from pressed steel, with one leg fitted with a steel point, while the other adjustable leg holds a short pencil. They can be used for drawing circles or arcs, but are more often used for fitting a wooden member to an irregular surface, as shown in Figure 3:29.

Dividers also are similar to the compass, but differ in that both legs are of solid metal. They are usually equipped

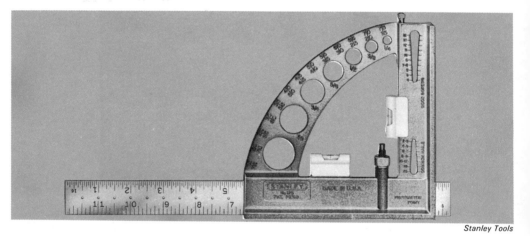

Stanley Tools

Fig. 3:26   All-in-one Measuring Tool

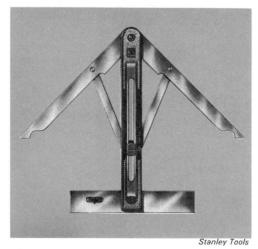

Stanley Tools

Fig. 3:27   Angle Dividers

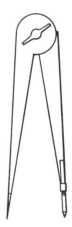

Fig. 3:28   Scribers

with a spring tension bar that has an adjusting screw and locking device to maintain the divider setting once a precision measurement has been made. Dividers are generally used for stepping off distances or equal spaces from a rule or for making more accurate layouts than can be made with a compass. Dividers or compasses can be used for laying out such geometric forms as triangles, hexagons, and octagons. The method of laying out these forms is shown in Figures 3:33 and 3:34.

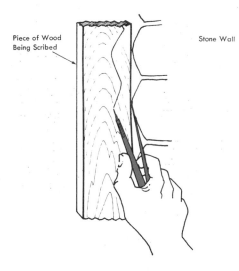

Fig. 3:29   Scribing to an Irregular Surface

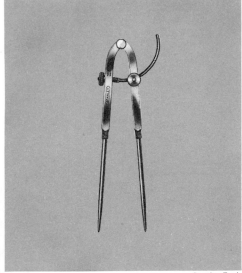

Stanley Tools

Fig. 3:30   Wing Dividers

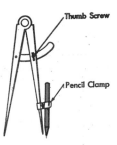

Fig. 3:31   Combination Dividers and Compass

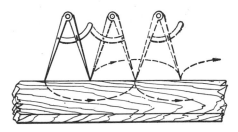

Fig. 3:32   Marking Off Distances with Dividers

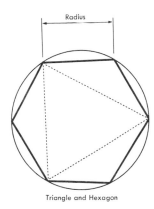

Fig. 3:33   Laying Out a Triangle and a Hexagon Using a Pair of Dividers or a Compass

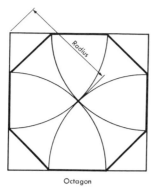

Octagon

Fig. 3:34 Laying Out an Octagon Using Dividers or Compass

Trammel points are used for making large arcs and circles of almost any size. They consist of two metal frames fitted with metal points or a pencil. The frames can be clamped onto a light wooden strip of any length, referred to as the beam.

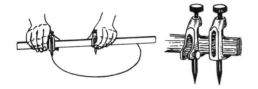

Stanley Tools

Fig. 3:35 Trammel Points

ASSIGNMENT

1. What are the units of linear measurement used in woodworking? List some other units of linear measurement.
2. (a) How many sixteenths of an inch are there in $3\frac{3}{16}$"?
   (b) How many thirty-seconds of an inch are there in $2\frac{5}{32}$"?
3. List four types of rules.
4. What is the advantage of placing a rule on edge when measuring?
5. List eight layout tools.
6. What is the principal purpose of a try square?
7. List four uses of the combination square.
8. Why should you check the setting of a marking gauge with a rule?
9. What is the main purpose of a marking gauge? of a mortise gauge?
10. Explain how a piece of stock can be marked with a scriber to fit an irregular surface.
11. For what purpose are trammel points used?
12. Using a compass and rule, lay out a hexagon and an octagon on a page of your notebook.

CHAPTER FOUR

framing square

The *framing square*, or *steel square*, as it is sometimes called, is a tool of many uses. It is used extensively by carpenters for layouts of rafters and stairs, and for other structural layouts. In fact, it is difficult to imagine a building of any type being constructed without the use of the framing square. This tool is also used extensively in most of the other building trades. Because of its importance, it is described in some detail in this chapter.

Most framing squares are of a standard size, although some have more information engraved on them than others. The finish also varies; it may be blued, polished, copper-finished, or nickel-plated. The square consists of two arms that meet at right angles to each other. The long arm is called the *body* or, sometimes, the *blade*; it is 24" long and 2" wide. The shorter arm is called the *tongue* and is 16" long and 1½" wide. The outer edge where the tongue and the body meet is called the *heel*. The square has a *face* and a *back*. The face side is the one with the manufacturer's name stamped on it.

Because the square is extensively used for layout work, its edges are marked off in various fractions of an inch, such as thirty-seconds, sixteenths, twelfths, tenths, and eighths. These are referred to as *scales*.

Figure 4:1 illustrates the location on the square where the various tables and scales are to be found. For fine dimensions a scale marked in ¹/₁₀₀ " divisions is also provided. It is placed on the back of the tongue near the heel. If a dimension in hundredths of an inch is required, the distance can be stepped off with the dividers and added to the

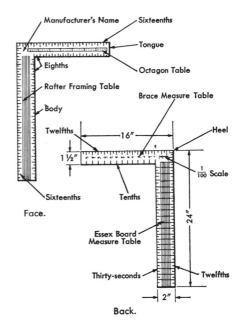

Fig. 4:1   Framing Square

whole numbers required.

When you first look at a good framing square and see all the markings, tables, and scales engraved on it, they may appear to be a meaningless mass of figures. However, they all have meaning and are not difficult to use once you understand them. The more you use the square, the more expert you will become with it.

Essex board measure

On the centre section of the back of the blade is a series of numbers known as the *Essex board measure*. This is a table that is not nearly as complicated as it first appears. It is used to determine quickly and easily the number of board feet of lumber in a piece of stock

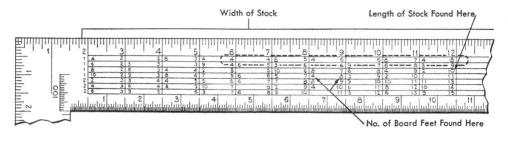

Fig. 4:2   Essex Board Measure

of a given size. The figures used in the table are based on lumber 1″ thick. Other lumber thicknesses can be calculated accordingly. The width of the piece of stock will be represented by the inch graduations on the scale on the outer edge of the blade, and the length in feet by the numbers under the 12″ graduation on the same scale. The number of board feet will be found under the figure representing the width and on the line representing the length. This amount is given in feet and twelfths of a foot, the figure on the left of the long line indicating the feet and the figure on the right the twelfths. Study Figure 4:2.

Example: Find the number of board feet in a piece of stock 1″ thick, 8″ wide, and 9′ long.

We would begin by looking under the 12″ graduation on the scale on the outer edge. On the second line below it will be found the figure 9, which in this case represents the length. Follow this line along to the left until you reach the column of figures under the 8″ mark. The figure 6 appears on the second line. Thus there are 6 board feet in this piece of stock.

If the stock were 10′ long and 8″ wide, you would look in the line below and find the answer to be $6\,9/12$ board feet. If the stock were 2″ thick the answer would be doubled.

Due to the lack of space, only part of the complete Essex board measure table is stamped on the framing square.

You will notice that there are only seven lines in the table representing seven lengths of stock. However, any multiple or fraction of these lengths can be used. For example, if the stock were 16′ long, the number of board feet given for a piece 8′ long would be doubled, or if it were 4′ long, the number of board feet would be halved.

Some arithmetic will be required to find the number of board feet in stock in which the width is not in even inches. For example, if a piece were 8½″ wide, the number of board feet for 8″ material would be subtracted from the number of board feet for the 9″ piece and one-half the result added to the figure found for the 8″ width. The same procedure would be followed to determine the board feet in a piece of stock the length of which is in a fraction of a foot, such as 10½′ long.

Rafter framing table

The rafter framing table appears on the face of the body of the square. This table is used to determine the length of common, hip, valley, and jack rafters for roof framing. Its use is not described here because a study of roof framing is required before it can be understood.

Brace measure

On the back of the centre section of the tongue of the square is found a se-

ries of numbers known as the *brace measure* (Figure 4:3). This table tells us accurately and quickly the length required for a brace between a beam and a post when the run and the rise are known. The run is the distance along the beam or horizontal member, and the rise is the distance on the post or vertical member (see Figure 4:4).

Fig. 4:3 Brace Measure Table

You will notice the series of figures on the table read from the right $\frac{18}{24}$ 30, $\frac{60}{60}$ 84.85, $\frac{57}{57}$ 80.61, and so on, with different sets of figures at 3″ intervals along the square, as shown in Figure 4:3. The first two figures in each set represent the run and the rise, and the third number the length of the brace at its longest point. The distance stated on the table for the run and the rise is in most cases the same. The reason for this is that most braces used are at a 45° angle, which is the most efficient angle for a brace. However, the set of figures in this table closest to the heel gives distances of 18 and 24, which is a common short-brace size. Any multiple of these figures can be used, such as 36 and 48, which would require a brace twice 30″, or 60″, long. For a 6″ and 8″ distance on the beam and the post, the brace length would be ¹⁄₃ of 30″, or 10″ long. Any multiple of the other sets of figures can also be used for determining brace lengths.

The information given in this table is based on the length of the hypotenuse of a 90° triangle. The same results could be obtained by using the Pythagorean theorem.

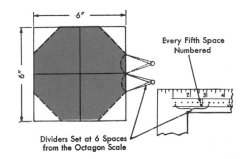

Fig. 4:4 Post, Beam, and Brace

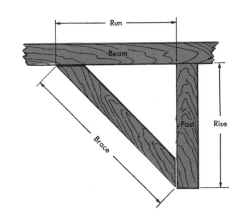

Fig. 4:5 Laying Out an Octagon

Octagon table

The octagon table is stamped on the face of the tongue and consists of two lines with a series of dots between them. With this table it is easy to lay out accurately an octagon, or eight-sided figure. Suppose you require an octagon that is 6″ across. First draw a 6″ square. Now draw lines through the centre dividing it into four equal parts. With the dividers step off six spaces (one space for each inch of width) from the octagon table, starting from the first dot. Step this distance off on your layout from each centre line as shown in Figure 4:4. Join up the points you have just located to form the octagon.

19

Polygon Table

Name	Number of sides	On the body use	On the tongue use
PENTAGON	5	12	8 ¾
HEXAGON	6	12	6 15/16
SEPTAGON	7	12	5 ¾
OCTAGON	8	12	5

Laying out polygons

The octagon table is designed only for the layout of eight-sided figures. However, figures with other numbers of sides can be laid out with the framing square if the length of the side is known. A *regular polygon* is a many-sided figure with all sides and angles equal. The names given to the various kinds of polygons indicate the number of sides each has. For example, a pentagon has five sides, a hexagon six, a septagon seven, and an octagon eight. The mitre or angle cut required for these can be laid out by using the correct numbers on the body and the tongue of the square. The numbers to be used are shown in the following table for the most frequently used regular polygons.

How the layout is made is shown in Figure 4:6. The square is laid on the work with the figures listed on the table for the desired polygon on the edge of the work. Mark along the tongue. Then reverse the square and mark along the tongue again at the required length for the side; always mark along the tongue side of the square. Lay out and cut the number of pieces necessary for the sides of the polygon frame being made. If you wish to lay out a polygon on a large flat surface, follow the same procedure.

Bisecting an angle

It is often necessary to bisect an angle, that is, to divide it into two equal parts. This can be done with the framing square, as shown in Figure 4:7. Be sure to use the same number on both the tongue and the body of the square.

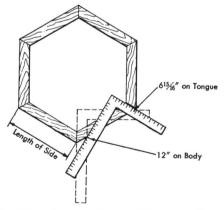

6 15/16" on Tongue

Length of Side

12" on Body

Fig. 4:6   Laying Out a Hexagon Frame Using a Framing Square

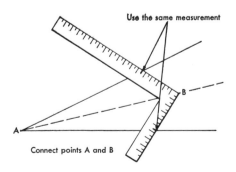

Use the same measurement

A

B

Connect points A and B

Fig. 4:7   Bisecting an Angle

Finding the centre of a circle

Simply place the square on the circle with the heel touching the circumference at any point. Make a mark on the circle where the arm of the square crosses it, as shown in Figure 4:8. Draw a line between these two points. Reset the square at any other point on the circle and draw another line. The point of intersection will be the exact centre of the circle.

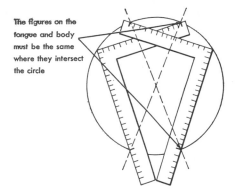

The figures on the tongue and body must be the same where they intersect the circle

Fig. 4:8 Finding the Centre of a Circle

Drawing a circle

You may wish to draw a circle on a flat wood surface and not have a compass handy. To make a circle with a framing square, draw the centre line of the circle, measure the required diameter of the circle along this line, and drive a nail in at each of the two points. Place the square against the nails, as shown in Figure 4:9. Hold a pencil on the heel of the square and slide the square on the nails so that a semi-circle is drawn. Reverse the square and draw the other half of the circle.

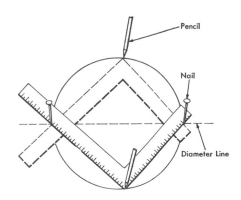

Pencil

Nail

Diameter Line

Fig. 4:9 Drawing a Circle Using a Framing Square

Drawing an ellipse

A useful geometric shape that can be constructed with a framing square and one that cannot be made with a compass is an oval, or ellipse. The size of an ellipse is determined by the major and minor axes, which are the large and small diameters of the figure. Mark the centre lines on the material on which the ellipse is to be drawn, and mark on the axes, as shown in Figure 4:10. Place the square on the layout with the tongue on the minor axis centre line and the body on the major axis centre line. Take a light piece of wood approximately ½″ × 1½″ and 3″ longer than half the length of the major axis. Drill a small hole for a pencil point 1½″ from one end of the piece. From the centre of this hole measure along the

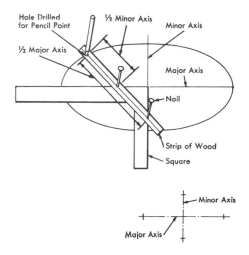

Hole Drilled for Pencil Point

½ Minor Axis

Minor Axis

½ Major Axis

Major Axis

Nail

Strip of Wood

Square

Minor Axis

Major Axis

Fig. 4:10 Drawing an Ellipse

stick a distance equal to half the minor axis and drive a nail at this point. For the second nail, measure from the pencil hole along the piece a distance equal to half the major axis. Let the nail point project ⅛" through the piece. Place the stick over the square with one nail point resting against the tongue of the square and the other against the body and with a pencil in the hole in the end of the stick. One-quarter of the ellipse can be drawn by allowing the nail points to slide along the two edges of the square, as in Figure 4:10. The other three-quarters of the ellipse can be drawn in the same manner.

The principal use of the framing square in the building industry is for layout operations such as roof and stair framing. To use the square for these purposes intelligently requires considerable knowledge of building construction and is, therefore, not dealt with in this book.

ASSIGNMENT

1. Make two drawings of a framing square, one showing the face, the other showing the back. Name the parts and their sizes, and show where on the square each scale is located and where the various tables are to be found.
2. Describe how you would lay out a line 6.47" long, using the framing square.
3. What is the purpose of the Essex board measure table on the framing square?
4. Using the sketch of the part of the square shown here, state the number of board feet in the following pieces of lumber:
   (a) 2 pieces 1" × 9" × 8'
   (b) 4 pieces 2" × 9" × 11'
   (c) 8 pieces 1" × 10" × 12'
   (d) 6 pieces 1" × 9½" × 14'
5. Why is the number 12 not included in the column of figures represent-

8	9	10	11	12	13	14
5.4	6	6.8	7.4	8	8.8	9.4
6	6.9	7.6	8.3	9	9.9	10.6
6.8	7.6	8.4	9.2	10	10.10	11.8
7.4	8.3	9.2	10.1	11	11.11	12.10
8.8	9.9	10.10	11.11	13	14.1	15.2
9.4	10.6	11.8	12.10	14	15.2	16.4
10	11.3	12.6	13.9	15	16.3	17.6

ing the length of pieces in the Essex board measure table?

6. What is meant by the terms *rise* and *run* in connection with the brace measure table?

7. From the following sketch, list the length of the brace required, where (a) the run is 57 — rise is 57, (b) the run is 20 — rise is 20, (c) the run is 9 — rise is 12.

8. Explain how an octagon is laid out using the octagon table on the square.

9. What is the definition of a regular polygon?

10. List the names of the following regular polygons: (a) a 5-sided figure; (b) a 6-sided figure; (c) a 7-sided figure; and (d) an 8-sided figure.

11. Explain how you would use the information on the polygon table to lay out a septagon.

12. Using the framing square, bisect an angle either in your notebook or on a piece of wood.

13. In how many positions must the square be placed in order to find the centre of a circle?

14. By means of a sketch, show how to draw a circle on a wood surface with the framing square.

15. List the steps required to draw an ellipse with a framing square.

wood as a material

Wood has always been one of our most abundant and most valuable raw materials. To primitive man it meant shelter, utensils, fuel, and weapons, and men soon learned that wood could be shaped and that several pieces could be joined together to make all manner of useful things. With the advance of technology other materials have replaced wood for some purposes, but there has been, at the same time, a very large increase in the number and variety of new products manufactured from wood or wood fibres. We need only think of paper, plywood, plastics, veneer, wallboards, fabrics, and adhesives to see how our use of wood has grown. It would, in fact, be difficult to imagine our way of life without wood.

Some of the reasons for the usefulness and popularity of wood products are: the ease with which it can be worked with hand tools and machines to any desired shape or size; the strength of wood in proportion to its weight; the ability of wood to absorb shock from a suddenly applied load; the pleasing appearance of the colour, texture, and grain formation; the durability and performance of wood; and the high insulation value of wood with respect to heat, sound, and electrical current. Wood can easily be fastened together with nails, screws, dowels, or glue; it can easily be bent or twisted for various uses; it takes and holds paint well; and it can be salvaged and re-used several times. Because an adequate supply of wood is available in most parts of the world, wood is the most economical structural material. One of the principal advantages of wood is that forests are renewable like crops, so that, with care

and conservation, a continuous supply of lumber remains available. This requires an efficient forest management policy to maintain these areas as a permanent source of raw materials for the forest-based industries that supply us with lumber and other wood products. Our forests should also be developed as a setting for a wide range of recreational activities.

Our forests are not unlimited. The world's demand for lumber has been so great that our once-abundant supply has already been sadly depleted. In order to meet the ever-increasing call on our forest resources, the following steps must be taken:

(a) Lumbering operations should be selective; only mature trees should be cut.

(b) Seedlings should be planted immediately after an area has been cropped.

(c) New crops must be tended in order to achieve maximum growth for the greatest possible quality and quantity of good trees.

(d) Adequate protection must be provided against forest fires and insects.

(e) New strains and species of trees must be developed that are suited to our soil and climate and will grow to maturity in a short time.

If our forests are not properly managed, the needs of future generations will not be met; it is as simple as that.

Lumber

When wood is cut into commercial sizes it is referred to as lumber. In Canada there are 170 different species of trees; 55 of these are used commercially; 23 are hardwood varieties. Of all the wood used in Canada today 20% is for fuel, 34% for pulp and paper, 42% for lumber, and 4% for miscellaneous uses. We are primarily concerned in this book with the 42% of the wood that is cut into lumber.

All Canadian lumber can be divided into two general classifications, *softwood* and *hardwood*.

Softwood is cut from those trees we commonly call evergreens, which keep their needle-like foliage all winter. Because most of these trees produce cones, they are also called conifers.

Hardwood is cut from broad-leafed trees that lose their leaves in the winter. They are referred to as deciduous trees. Some common species of hardwoods are ash, oak, birch, walnut, and elm.

Hardwoods and softwoods are fundamentally the same, being made of the same substance. All wood consists of millions of tiny, hollow cells packed tightly together in a honeycomb structure. Hardwoods, however, have a thicker cell wall, making the wood denser and heavier, thus increasing its strength. Softwoods, on the other hand, have thin cell walls, which makes them more porous and lighter in weight and therefore not as strong as hardwood. The woods that we use vary in density from 20 to 50 pounds per cubic foot when dry and have a corresponding variation in strength. The terms *soft* and *hard* are only general ones, for there are the exceptional softwoods that are harder than some woods classed as hardwoods.

In general, softwoods are easier to work, more resistant to rot, and strong enough for general purposes. Because of these qualities and the fact that they are plentiful and relatively inexpensive, softwoods such as spruce, hemlock, and cedar are used extensively in the construction of homes and other buildings. Fortunately for us, seventy-five per cent of the forests of the northern hemisphere are the softwood variety.

Hardwoods are extensively used for furniture because they are harder and stronger, have a more attractive grain formation, and in many cases are darker in colour. Hardwood is also used for many purposes in buildings where extra strength, greater wearing qualities, or a more attractive appearance is required, as in floors, trim, and stairs.

To transform a living tree into usable lumber involves many operations. The tree must be felled, the branches trimmed off, and the log transported to the sawmill. The bark sections, referred to as *slabs*, must be removed. The part of the log suitable for lumber is then sawed into boards generally 1" or 2" in thickness. The lumber must then be stacked for seasoning until it is dry enough for commercial use, or it may be artificially dried in kilns immediately after being cut. The latter method permits the lumber to be put on the market much sooner and also saves shipping weight. The lumber is generally dressed or planed smooth on two or all of its four surfaces before it is ready for the customer. The parts of the tree not used for lumber are often cut into chips to be pressed into wallboard or ground into pulp for paper.

The lumbering industry is now becoming highly mechanized. Heavy equipment can trim off all the limbs and top while the tree is still standing, cut it at ground level, and load the log onto a waiting truck.

Structure of wood

A general knowledge of the structure of wood and the various growth formations that make up the wood we use is essential in understanding how to use it. Wood reacts in certain ways under

25

certain conditions because of its structure.

A quarter-section of a log is shown in Figure 5:1, illustrating some of these growth formations.

Bark

No two species of tree have identical bark, a factor that makes it easier to identify trees. The bark is the outer protective coating. If much of this bark is removed, the tree will die. The bark consists of a thick outer *cortex layer* and an inner *bast layer*.

Cambium layer

This is the very important fibrous layer of the tree where all the growth takes place. New cells of both sapwood and bark are constantly being formed in this layer. All the food for the growth of the tree, moving either up or down, is transported within the cambium layer.

Annual rings

The growth that takes place each year is evident from the formation of these rings of vertical cells. They are made up of a wide, light-coloured section, the *spring wood*, which is the growth that takes place in the spring. The other part is the narrow harder section, the *summer wood*, which is formed in the summer when the growth is relatively slow. The sizes of the rings vary according to the growing conditions in that particular year. The rings are much larger in those species of tree that grow quickly.

Medullary rays

These are rows of small wood cells that grow horizontally from the centre of the tree towards the bark. They bind the annual rings together, greatly strengthening the tree. The medullary rays are apparent in hardwoods, such as oak, but are not visible in most softwoods. They transport the flow of sap

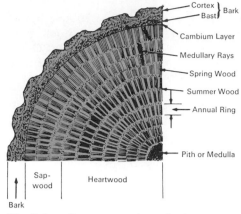

Fig. 5:1   Quarter-section of a Log

from the outer to the inner part of the sapwood sections of the tree.

Pith or medulla

This is the core of the log. In a healthy tree it is hard, but as the tree gets older it becomes soft and eventually begins to decay. The decay spreads to the rest of the tree until a hollow log develops.

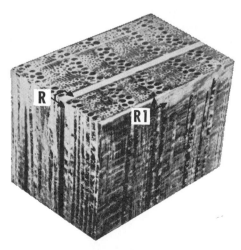

Forest Products Research Branch, Dept. of Forestry

Fig. 5:2   Cell Structure—Enlarged View of an Oak Block Showing Four Annual Layers. Note the large, porous wood cells in the spring wood and the smaller cells in the summer wood. The medullary ray is shown at R and R1.

Sapwood

This wood is made up of the living cells of the tree. It is generally lighter in colour than the heartwood and has fewer knots.

Heartwood

The cells in this section have ceased to function as part of the living tree. Yet, generally the wood is hard and sound, and darker in colour than the sapwood.

Lumber quality

There are almost as many qualities and grades of lumber as there are uses for it. Some wood is good only for firewood. Poor-quality lumber is used for crating or other rough work; the better lumber is used for furniture or trim.

Below is a list of some of the defects and blemishes found in lumber that make for poor quality. A lumber *defect* is a condition that affects the strength and appearance of a piece of stock. A *blemish* is a condition that affects only the appearance of the lumber.

Knots

These are not necessarily injurious to the lumber unless they are loose and likely to drop out. Too many knots, however, even when sound and tight, lower the grade of the lumber because they can affect its strength and appearance.

Wane

When bark appears on the edge of lumber the result is an uneven edge and a low grade of lumber.

Pitch pockets

These are cavities in the lumber that are filled with pitch. If they are numerous, they are considered to be a serious defect. Pitch pockets occur most often in pine and fir.

Stain streaks

These are streaks of discoloration caused by minerals in the soil, seasoning, or slight decay. They should be considered as blemishes rather than defects and are not serious if the work is to be painted.

Dry rot

This is a fungus growth that forms on wood when it is placed in a dry, warm place with little ventilation. It seriously affects the strength of lumber.

Worm holes

These are caused by termites or other wood-eating insects that bore through the wood. They can make lumber very unsightly and sometimes affect its strength.

Wet rot

Rot is caused by a fungus growth when the wood is in constant contact with warm air and moisture. It is very injurious to lumber.

Shakes

Shakes, which are caused by frost or wind in living trees or by injury when a tree is felled, consist of a separation of the wood fibres. Three types of shakes exist: (a) *ring shakes*, a separation between the growth rings; (b) *transverse shakes*, a separation running across the wood fibres; and (c) *through shakes*, where the check or crack extends all the way through the log.

Wood shrinkage and warpage

One of the problems that we must face when using wood is that it is constantly changing in shape and volume. How much and at what rate wood will shrink or swell depends on how much moisture the wood contains. Freshly sawed wood contains a great deal of moisture;

lumber that has been seasoned contains little. The moisture content of the air surrounding lumber will also determine the amount of shrinkage or swelling that takes place. Wood gives up moisture and shrinks under low humidity or dry conditions and takes in moisture and swells under high humidity or moist air conditions.

The moisture that causes these changes is stored in the walls of the minute wood cells. Figure 5:3 shows three very much enlarged views of one of these cells. *A* is a cell from freshly cut green lumber. Both the cell wall and the cavity in the centre are saturated with moisture. *B* shows the same cell after some of the moisture has gone out of the lumber, leaving the centre of the cell empty. No change has yet taken place in the size of the cell. In *C* the wood has dried still further, and the moisture has left the wall as well as the centre of the cell, making it smaller. The drying out of the millions of individual cells causes the lumber to shrink in width and thickness but very little in length.

The moisture in the wood exists in two forms: (a) *free*, the water occupying the hollow space in the wood cell; and (b) *hygroscopic*, the moisture held in the material composing the cell wall. When the free water in the hollow area evaporates but the walls are still saturated, the wood is considered to be at its *fibre saturation point*. This generally occurs when the wood reaches a moisture content of 25 per cent.

When wood is stored for some time in a place where the temperature and the relative humidity of the air are constant the wood will reach the same moisture content as the air surrounding it. When this condition is reached the wood is at its *equilibrium moisture content*, after which no shrinking or swelling should occur, unless the moisture content of the air surrounding it

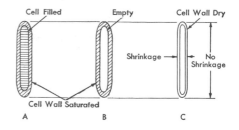

Fig. 5:3   Wood Cell Shrinkage

changes.

Some of this shrinkage can be minimized by the way the log is sawed into boards. The two methods generally used are *plain sawed* (flat grain) and *quarter sawed* (edge grain). These are illustrated in Figures 5:4 and 5:5. The largest amount of usable lumber can be obtained from plain sawed logs. Although this results in less wastage,

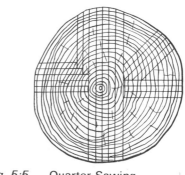

Fig. 5:4   Plank and Log Shrinkage

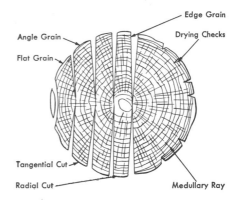

Fig. 5:5   Quarter Sawing

the quality is not as high as for lumber cut from quarter sawed logs.

The medullary rays prevent the wood from shrinking at a right angle to the rings. Thus, if the lumber is cut with the rings running through the thickness of the piece, as shown in Figure 5:5 for quarter sawed lumber, warpage is reduced to a minimum. The board will shrink in thickness but very little in width. It should be noted here that the shrinking or swelling of the wood cells determines the amount of warping or cupping of a flat sawed board. This is due to the direction of the medullary rays. Because very little shrinkage takes place along these rays, the piece shrinks more on one face than on the other. Thus we often find warped boards with a hollow centre, as shown in Figure 5:6.

Flat-grained woods present an attractive wide grain formation but have the disadvantage of changing shape. Edge-grained woods on the other hand may not present as attractive an appearance, but they will stay flat. For this reason, they are used for such things as stair treads, where a permanent flat surface is essential.

All woods will check or crack a certain amount at the end of the log or board. The checking takes place along the medullary rays as the wood dries out. The moisture leaves through the end grain more rapidly, causing the board to shrink faster at this point and the end to split or check.

Definition of types of warpage

Figure 5:7 illustrates the following kinds of warping:

(a) cup — bending of a side across the grain,

(b) bow — bending of a side along the grain of wood,

(c) crook — bending of an edge along the grain of wood,

(d) twist or wind — bending of sides and edges of a piece of wood (propeller shape).

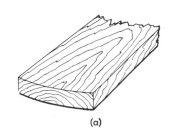

(a)

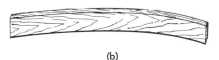

(b)

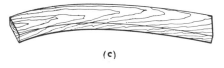

(c)

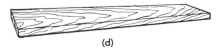

(d)

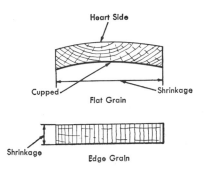

Fig. 5:6   Board Shrinkage

Fig. 5:7   Types of Warpage

Seasoning of wood

Before lumber is used, it should be carefully dried to bring it to the correct moisture content. This will minimize any shrinkage or warping that might take place when it is used, and will also increase the strength and hardness of the lumber. This carefully controlled drying of lumber is referred to as seasoning.

There are two methods of seasoning lumber: air drying and kiln drying.

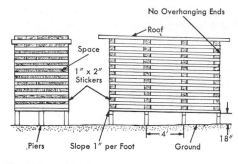

Fig. 5:8 Air Seasoning

Air drying

Lumber to be air dried is stacked in piles in the open air (see Figure 5:8). The boards must be placed so that there is a free circulation of air between the pieces and each layer of boards. The pile must be set on blocks or piers. Lumber is placed as a roof on the top of the pile at a slope to allow the rain to run off. The weight of the boards above prevents undue warpage in the pile. The length of time required to dry lumber in this manner depends on the temperature and the moisture content of the air, as well as on the use to which the lumber is to be put. Air-dried lumber is suitable for construction and general use.

Kiln drying

Lumber can also be dried in an enclosure called a *kiln*. There are many sizes and shapes of these. One type is shown in Figure 5:9 and illustrates the general principles of the process. Hot air is forced up through the centre of the pile, which has been carefully constructed to ensure a circulation of air, and the cool air is drawn off from around the outside of the pile. This circulation of warm air draws the moisture from the wood.

The humidity of the air must be controlled in order not to dry the wood too rapidly, thus causing it to check or be-

come honeycombed. In a kiln the moisture content of lumber can be closely controlled so that it can be dried to suit any type of work from outside framework to fine furniture. The temperature of the kiln is kept at approximately 180°F. The length of drying time depends on the desired moisture content of the wood. The moisture content desirable for lumber used for furniture and cabinet work is 4% to 6%, for interior trim 6% to 8%, and for structural framework 10% to 20%. Most lumber mills use moisture meters to determine the percentage of moisture in their lumber.

The kiln shown in Figure 5:9 is a simple compartment *charge kiln*. Larger kilns are also used, where the lumber is loaded on rolling cars that enter at

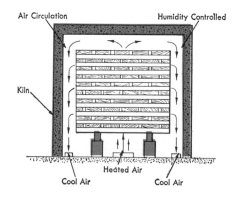

Fig. 5:9 Kiln Drying

one end of a long tunnel, and the lumber is dried as it passes through to the other end. Many carloads of lumber can be seasoned at the same time in this way. These are referred to as *progressive kilns*. The smaller type of charge kilns often use a natural flow of warm air, while the larger kilns use forced-air heating. There are other methods of artificially seasoning lumber, most of them still in the experimental stage. Some are used for small lots of lumber in the manufacture of special, expensive wood products. These methods may involve the use of chemical seasoning, high-frequency dielectric heating, infra-red radiation, solvent seasoning, vacuum drying, or vapour drying.

Wood identification

Because there are hundreds of different species of wood, it is impossible here to provide a sure-fire method of identifying individual woods. The ability to identify a large number of woods comes only after considerable study and experience. Everyone, however, should be able to identify our most common woods. Some of these are illustrated on the inside covers of this book. How many of these can you recognize without looking at the labels? If not many, it would be worth your while to study them until you are familiar with all of these much-used woods.

In general, the softwoods have a small closed cell structure with a fine grain, while most hardwoods have a larger open grain and a coarse, wavy grain structure.

You will note that some of the distinguishing features of wood are the weight, colour, odour, cell structure, and grain formation. Standing trees are distinguished by their bark, leaves, seeds, flowers, nuts, and to some extent their size and habitat.

ASSIGNMENT

Wood as a material

1. Make a list of products that are made from wood pulp or wood fibres.
2. List five reasons for the popularity of wood as a material from which to make things.
3. State two ways in which you think we could conserve our forests.
4. (a) How many different species of tree grow in this country?
   (b) How many are commercially grown?
   (c) What percentage of the wood cut in our forests is used for lumber?
5. List four operations required to transform a living tree into lumber.
6. (a) Draw a cross-section of a log, showing the growth formation.
   (b) Write a sentence describing four of the growth formations just named.
7. (a) List three types of lumber defects, and state the cause of each.
   (b) List two types of blemishes found in lumber.
8. (a) Explain the difference between hard and soft wood.
   (b) State three uses for hardwood and three for softwood.
   (c) List three species of tree in each division.

Wood shrinkage and warpage

9. Show by means of a sketch how a wood cell in freshly cut lumber differs from one in well-seasoned lumber.
10. What is the difference between plain sawed lumber and quarter-sawed lumber?
11. (a) Redraw the pieces of lumber illustrated below, showing how they

might warp when they dry out.
(b) Why will they warp in the manner you have shown?

12. Why is edge-grained stock used in preference to flat-grained stock for some purposes?

Seasoning of wood

13. What is meant by the "seasoning" of wood?

14. Write a paragraph describing each of the two methods of seasoning lumber.

15. What should be the moisture content of lumber used for (a) furniture; (b) interior trim; (c) framework?

16. List four species of softwood trees and four species of hardwood trees.

17. What are some of the distinguishing features of the various species of woods that will help you to identify them?

18. Bring sample pieces of two hardwoods and two softwoods to class.

project design, bill of material, and lumber calculations

Any worth-while project requires considerable planning and a well-dimensioned drawing or a working model. The completed plan or model may be available to you. However, it will be more meaningful and give you more satisfaction if you design and possibly research the project to be made. This planning should involve creative design, including freehand sketches and investigation into the best material to be used, before a working drawing is made. For design details, see Chapter 29.

The ability to design useful woodworking projects will be of value to you whatever your line of work will be. This ability could well lead you into some branch of the important field of industrial design.

Bill of material

From the working drawings a *bill of material* should be made. It should be complete, listing each piece required, its exact thickness, width, and length, the type of wood, and its cost. An example of a bill of material for a small table is shown in Figure 6:1. A *rough stock list* or *cutting list* should then be made from the bill of material, allowing extra material for planing and squaring. The amount added will depend on the stock size of the lumber and whether or not the material from which the lumber is to be cut has been planed, or *dressed*. A general rule is to add ¼″ to the thickness and ¼″ to the width and ½″ to the length of each piece. The allowances for thickness are sometimes omitted when cutting from dressed lumber. For example, if the finished

NO. OF PIECES	NAME OF PART	THICK-NESS	WIDTH	LENGTH	TYPE OF WOOD
I	TOP	3/4"	18"	30"	BIRCH
2	RAILS	3/4"	2"	16"	BIRCH
2	RAILS	3/4"	2"	28"	BIRCH
4	LEGS	1 3/4"	1 3/4"	18"	BIRCH

Fig. 6:1   Typical Bill of Material

NO. OF PIECES	NAME OF PART	THICK-NESS	WIDTH	LENGTH	TYPE OF WOOD
3	TOP	7/8"	6 1/4"	30 1/2"	BIRCH
2	RAILS	7/8"	2 1/4"	16 1/2"	BIRCH
2	RAILS	7/8"	2 1/4"	28 1/2"	BIRCH
4	LEGS	1 7/8"	1 7/8"	18 1/2"	BIRCH

Fig. 6:2   Typical Cutting List. Sizes are taken from the bill of material in Fig. 6:1. Stock is to be cut from rough lumber.

size for a certain piece for a project is ¾″, no allowance would be made on the cutting list for thickness, since the finished stock size is ¾″. A cutting list is shown in Figure 6:2.

The correct order in stating the dimensions of lumber is (1) thickness, (2) width, and (3) length.

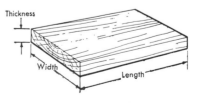

Fig. 6:3

The width of the lumber is always measured across the grain, the length is measured along the grain.

Lumber sizes and board feet

Much has already been said about the growth of trees and the nature of wood and how it is cut and seasoned for use. You should also be familiar with lumber measurements, terms, and grades, as well as the method of estimating board feet and lumber cost.

Lumber is cut from the log in standard thicknesses, widths, and lengths, which makes it convenient to store and to measure. The *stock size* or *nominal size* of boards is the size that is originally cut from the log. This is also known as the *rough size*. When it is dressed approximately ⅛" is taken off each planed surface. The nominal size into which lumber is cut is 1" or 2" thick and from 2" to 12" wide in 1" intervals, and in lengths of 8', 10', 12', 14', 16', and 18'. However, lumber is often sawed or planed to sizes other than these for special purposes.

Lumber is sold by the board foot, which is a piece 1" thick, 1' wide, and 1' long. The simple formula for calculating board feet is to multiply the thickness in inches by the width in feet by the length in feet. If the width or the length is given in inches, this must be divided by 12 to convert it to feet. For example, to calculate the number of board feet in a piece 1" × 8" × 12', the formula is:

$$1 \times \frac{8}{12} \times 12 = 8 \text{ board feet.}$$

Lumber that is less than 1" thick is generally considered to be the full inch thick when the board feet are worked out. For lumber that is more than 1" thick, the actual size is used in calculating the board feet. For example, a piece ⅝" × 6" × 12' would be considered as having 6 board feet, while a piece 1½" × 6" × 12' would have 9 board feet.

Lumber prices

Most lumber prices are based on a thousand feet (M). If oak is worth $250 per M, 400 board feet will cost

$$\frac{400 \times 250}{1000} = \$100.$$

Some lumber is sold by the linear, or running, foot. Examples of these materials are door trim (called casing by carpenters), baseboard, quarter round (which is placed along the baseboard at the floor level), and many other mouldings used in carpentry work. Many lumber mills also sell structural members such as 2" × 4" and 2" × 8" by the linear foot rather than by the board foot.

Plywood and wallboards are sold by the square foot, the price depending on the thickness and the quality.

Roofing shingles, made from either asphalt or wood, are measured in a different way, both types being sold by the square. A square of shingles is the quantity required to cover 100 square feet or an area 10' × 10'. They are packed in bundles, and the number of bundles to the square depends on the type of shingle.

Lumber is sold either in the rough or as dressed stock. A D.4.S. or S.4.S. may appear on a lumber bill, which indicates that the material is dressed or surfaced on four sides. Lumber may be dressed on two surfaces or four surfaces.

Grades of lumber

The grading of lumber is complicated and varies according to different standards and different types of wood. How-

Plain Fact

THE QUALITY OF YOUR WORK WILL DEPEND ON HOW WELL IT IS PLANNED. GOOD WORK REQUIRES GOOD PLANNING.

ever, in general it is graded from the best quality downward in this order: #1 Clear, #2 Clear, Selects, #1 Common, #2 Common, #3 Common, #4 Common, #5 Common, and #6 Common. In many cases the grades will be mixed; that is, the lumber will be labelled as Number 1 and 2 Common, meaning that there is some of each grade in the shipment. The number of defects or blemishes in the wood determines the grade.

ASSIGNMENT

1. State two reasons for making a bill of material.
2. What is the difference between a bill of material and a cutting list?
3. What order should be used in stating the dimensions of a piece of stock?
4. What are the advantages of cutting lumber into standard thickness, width, and length?
5. What does the abbreviation D.2.S. indicate when written on a lumber bill?
6. If the nominal size of a piece of stock is 2" × 8", what would its actual size be if it is D.4.S.?
7. What are the nominal sizes into which lumber is cut?

8. How many board feet would there be in each of these Items?
   (a) 4 pieces ½" × 8" × 12'
   (b) 3 pieces 1¼" × 10" × 14'
   (c) 5 pieces 2" × 9" × 20'
9. What would be the cost of (a), (b), and (c) in question 8 at $135 per M?
10. What would be the cost of quarter round for a room 8' 9" wide and 12' 6" long with one door 2' 8" wide at 4¢ per lineal foot?
11. What would be the cost of a sheet of ¾" × 4' × 8' plywood at 35¢ per foot?
12. How many squares of shingles will be required to cover both sides of a gable roof 26' long if the rafter length is 12'?
13. List in order the general grades of lumber.
14. Make out a complete bill of material and a cutting list for the nail box shown below.

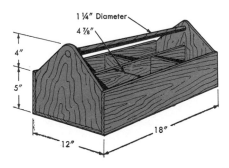

CHAPTER SEVEN

planes and planing

The plane is one of the most useful of all woodworking tools because it is so necessary for reducing stock to the correct size, as well as for making it smooth and square. To know the type and size of plane best suited for the job at hand and to know how to use a plane well is essential to all types of woodwork.

The first planes used were merely chisels placed in a wooden block. The blade was held in place at the correct depth by a wedge. Since those days many advances have been made in the manufacture of planes, and they are now produced in many different shapes and sizes, each suitable for a specific purpose. However, the principle of the cutting action is the same in all types.

Millers Falls Co.

Fig. 7:1   Jack Plane

Bench planes

The planes that are most often used in general woodwork are known as *bench planes*. They include the *smoothing*, *jack*, *fore*, and *jointer planes*. This type

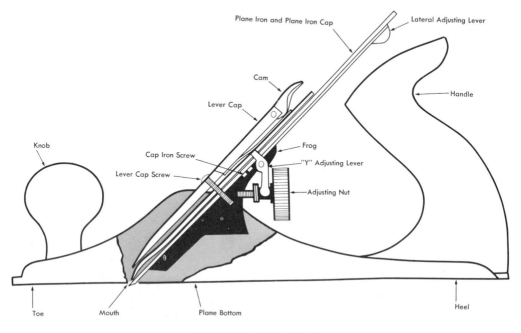

Fig. 7:2   Plane Parts

of plane is illustrated in Figures 7:1 and 7:2.

The *smoothing plane* is used for planing short stock smooth and flat. Its particular purpose, as its name implies, is to make a very smooth surface. It is often used to finish plane a board after it has been rough planed with a larger plane. The smoothing plane is generally 9" long and 2" wide, and has the same construction and design as the jack plane shown in Figure 7:1.

The *jack plane* is the general-purpose plane that is used more than any other. It is light enough to be handled easily, yet long enough to plane long stock if required. It is the plane that most carpenters carry in their tool boxes because it can be used for almost any planing operation. It is made in several sizes, but the one most used is 14" long and 2" wide (see Figure 7:1).

The *fore plane*, which is almost identical in construction with the jack plane, except that it is longer and wider, is used for planing longer material. Fore planes are usually 18" long and 2⅜" wide.

The *jointer plane* is the longest type of plane in general use and also is similar in construction to the jack plane. Because of its length, it is especially useful for truing the edges of long boards. Sizes range from 22" to 28" in

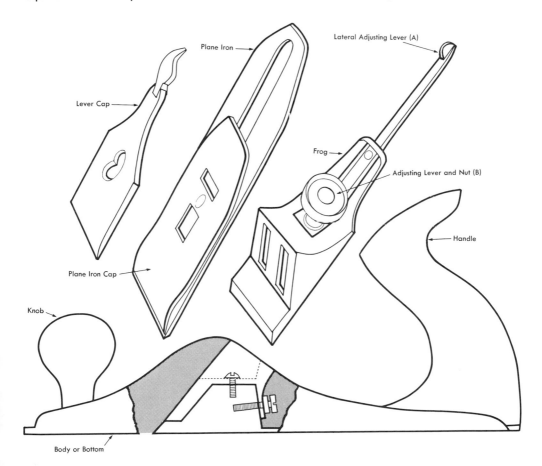

Plane Iron

Lateral Adjusting Lever (A)

Lever Cap

Frog

Adjusting Lever and Nut (B)

Handle

Plane Iron Cap

Knob

Body or Bottom

Fig. 7:3   Plane Parts

length and from 2⅜" to 2⅞" in width.

A cut-away view of a smoothing plane is shown in Figure 7:2, listing the parts, which are the same in almost all types of bench planes.

One of the secrets of the proper operation of a hand plane is to have it correctly adjusted for the depth of cut and the angle of the blade. There are two main blade adjustments on a hand plane: (1) the adjusting nut raises or lowers the blade and so regulates the amount of cut; (2) the lateral adjusting lever tilts the blade to the right or left. To set the plane blade, sight along the bottom of the plane and turn the adjusting nut until the sharp edge of the blade projects slightly above the sole of the plane. The lateral (sideways) adjustment of the blade can be checked at the same time by pushing the lever to the right or to the left until the blade is parallel with the plane bottom (see Figure 7:4).

Figures 7:5, 7:6, and 7:7 illustrate the correct method of assembling the blade and plane iron cap after cleaning or sharpening, to avoid dulling the cutting edge of the blade. The edge of the cap should be approximately ¹⁄₁₆" from the cutting edge of the blade, which should fit snugly down on the frog. The cam should be tight enough to hold the assembly firmly in place.

The plane iron cap is often referred to as the chip breaker because its main purpose is to stiffen and steady the blade so that the blade will cut a smooth, continuous shaving rather than chip shavings, which would occur if the blade were not held steady.

How to use a plane

The work should be held down firmly either between the jaws of a vise or

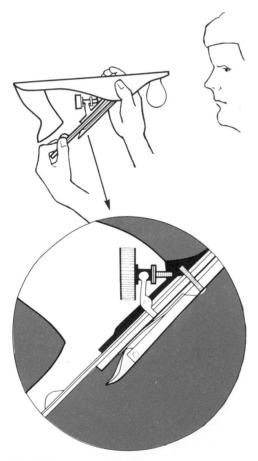

Fig. 7:4   Plane Adjustment

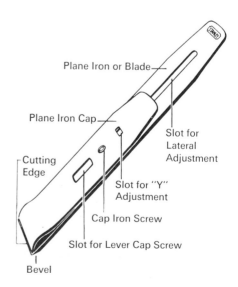

Plane Iron or Blade

Plane Iron Cap

Slot for Lateral Adjustment

Cutting Edge

Slot for "Y" Adjustment

Cap Iron Screw

Slot for Lever Cap Screw

Bevel

Fig. 7:5   Blade Assembly

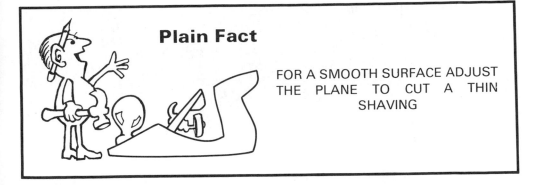

Plain Fact

FOR A SMOOTH SURFACE ADJUST THE PLANE TO CUT A THIN SHAVING

by using a bench stop. Both hands should be free to control and push the plane. Always plane in the direction of the grain. Cutting against the grain will result in an uneven, rough surface.

Hold the plane with the right hand on the handle and the left hand on the knob (reverse if left-handed). When beginning the cut, bear down firmly on the knob. As the plane stroke continues, place an even pressure on the handle and the knob. When finishing the stroke, lighten the pressure on the knob and bear down on the handle. This will prevent dubbing or rounding the end of the wood.

When planing the face of a board, a better cut is often produced by holding the plane at an angle to the edge of the board to make a shearing cut. This allows the plane blade to make a slicing cut that is narrower than the width of the blade. Thus we might have a 2" blade cutting a 1½" shaving (see Figure 7:8). Some planes are made with the blade set in the plane in such a way that it cuts at an angle to the direction of the stroke, thus making it possible to produce a shearing cut by pushing the plane parallel to the edge of the work.

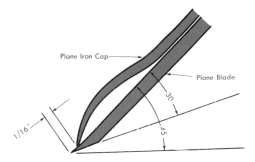

Fig. 7:6   Blade Assembly

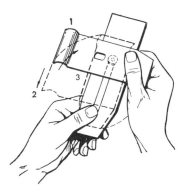

Fig. 7:7   Blade Assembly

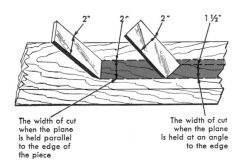

The width of cut when the plane is held parallel to the edge of the piece

The width of cut when the plane is held at an angle to the edge

Fig. 7:8   To make a shearing cut the plane blade should be at this angle.

Fig. 7:9

When planing the edge of the work, use as long a stroke as possible. The last few strokes should produce a shaving the full length and width of the piece. This will ensure a straight and true edge. If the piece is long, it is much better to use a long plane that will bridge the low spots and cut the high points until the edge is straight. Figures 7:9 and 7:10 illustrate this principle.

When planing end grain, make fine cuts with a sharp plane. See page 45 for three methods of planing end grain.

It is often necessary to cut a chamfer or a bevel on a board. The difference between these two terms, which are often confused, is illustrated in Figure 7:11. A *chamfer* is generally a 45° angle cut at the *arris* (the line where two surfaces meet at a 90° angle), and is generally made for decorative purposes. A *bevel* is cut the full thickness of the piece and at any angle. It is gen-

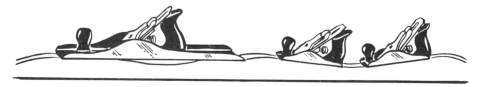

Fig. 7:10

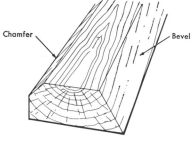

Fig. 7:11

erally made for some purpose other than decoration.

Both the chamfer and the bevel can best be cut with a plane after they have been laid out with a marking gauge or by gauging a line with a pencil, as shown in Figure 7:12. To do this, place your second finger against the edge of the stock and hold the pencil as shown. Practise drawing lines on a piece of scrap lumber. You will be surprised how easily and accurately it can be done. This method is much faster than the one requiring the use of the marking gauge.

Special planes

There are many special planes made for specific operations, some of which are shown in the following illustrations.

Fig. 7:12 Finger Gauging a Line

The *block plane* is made in varying sizes from 4" to 7" long, the most common size being 6" long with a blade 1⅝" wide. The block plane is used extensively for planing end grain, often by carpenters for fitting exterior and interior trim, but also for planing short pieces in the shop. This plane is made to be used with one hand, with the palm over the lever cap and the forefinger in the hollow of the finger rest. As shown in Figure 7:13 most block planes have an adjustable mouth.

A *rabbet plane* is used for cutting a recessed section out of the edge of a piece of stock. It is equipped with an adjustable depth gauge and a fence so that any desired size of rabbet can be cut.

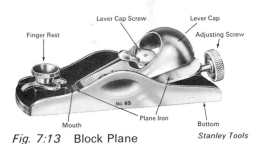

Fig. 7:13 Block Plane *Stanley Tools*

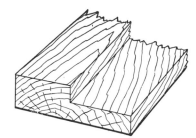

Stanley Tools

Fig. 7:14 Rabbet Plane

Fig. 7:15 Rabbet Cut

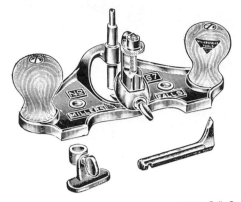

Millers Falls Co.

Fig. 7:16   Router Plane

The *router plane* is used to remove the waste material when making a groove, plough, or dado cut in a piece of stock. If the wide cut is parallel to the grain and on the side or face of the piece, it is called a *plough cut*. If it is on the edge of the stock, it is referred to as a *groove*. When the cut is at a right angle to the wood, it is a *dado* (see Figure 7:17). A saw or chisel is used to cut the boundary lines, while the router plane is used to take out the centre of the cut.

A new type of forming tool is shown in Figure 7:18. The cutting is done by a piece of steel mesh with sharp edges, which forms the bottom of the plane. The cutting surface is similar to that of a wood rasp. The blades are replaceable (Figure 7:19).

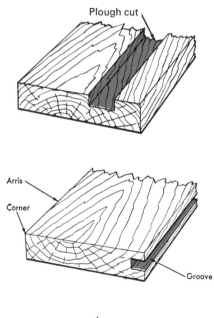

Stanley Tools

Fig. 7:18   Surform Tool

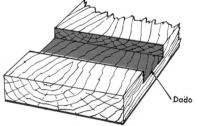

Fig. 7:17   These cuts can be made with a router plane.

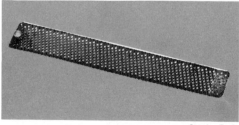

Stanley Tools

Fig. 7:19   Replaceable Blade

A *spokeshave* (Figure 7:20) can be considered as belonging to the plane family. The principle of the cutting action is the same; it is really a short-bottomed plane with a handle on each side, which makes it easy to push over curved surfaces. The spokeshave should be pushed away from the operator, so that it cuts on the downstroke, as illustrated in Figure 7:21. If this is not done, the blade tends to dig in or chatter. Spokeshaves are made with convex and concave bottoms, as well as with straight ones. The blade is adjusted by thumbscrews on the type shown, while on other types the blade must be tapped down to the correct setting.

Squaring stock

One of the chief purposes of a plane is to reduce stock to the correct size and shape, an operation often referred to as *squaring stock*, or *to true up stock*. More specifically, these terms mean to make a true rectangular shape with all surfaces flat, all corners square, all opposite sides parallel, and of the correct thickness, width, and length. To produce such a piece of stock simply requires the standard planing operations with which you may be quite familiar. However, to perform them well and in the proper sequence, testing each operation as it is completed, is an important step that you should learn to do automatically in the construction of most projects made from wood.

It is important that you plane the sides, edges, and ends of the board in order and at right angles to each other. Not all tradesmen perform the steps in the same sequence, but the same results must be achieved. The order of operations often used is as follows:

1. *Plane the face side*. After cutting the stock to rough length and width, select the better of the two broad surfaces (the one with the fewest blemishes or

Stanley Tools

Fig. 7:20   Spokeshave

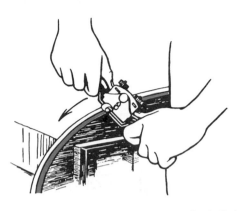
Stanley Tools

Fig. 7:21   Use of a Spokeshave to Cut a Chamfer on an Outside Curve

defects) and plane this surface flat and smooth. It can best be held in place for planing by using a vise, as shown in Figure 7:22. Plane always in the direction of the grain.

Test the surface for flatness with a try square or straightedge, as shown in Figure 7:23. Test the surface from edge to edge, from end to end, and diagonally from corner to corner. Mark this surface for the face side.

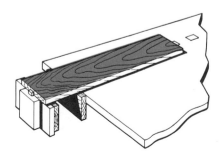

Fig. 7:22   Plane this face flat and smooth.

43

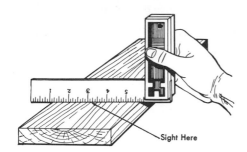

Fig. 7:23 Testing for Flatness

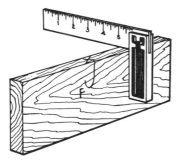

Wind Sticks of Identical Size

Fig. 7:24 Testing for Wind

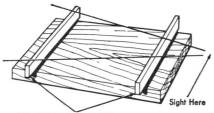

Fig. 7:25 Testing an Edge to the Face

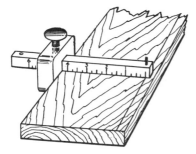

Fig. 7:26 Scribing Stock to Width

In some cases it is necessary to test the face surface of a board for *wind* (*twist* or *propeller shape*). This can be done by placing two straight-edged sticks of identical widths on the face of the piece, as shown in Figure 7:24. Sight over the tops of the wind sticks. If they are in line with each other, the piece is true and free from wind or twist.

2. *Plane the face edge*. Choose the better edge and place the piece in the vise with this edge up. Plane the edge straight and smooth by taking full-length cuts. Use a straightedge to test from end to end for straightness and a try square to determine if the edge is square to the face side.

Identifying check marks are sometimes used to indicate the face side and face edge. They generally consist of a mark with a loop on the face side and an X on the face edge, one end of which joins up with the loop on the face (see Figure 7:25).

3. *Cut and plane to width*. Set the marking gauge to the required width of the stock. From the face edge just planed, scribe a line on the face side the full length of the stock, as shown in Figure 7:26. If there is more than ⅜″ of stock to be removed, it may be necessary to cut off some of the surplus with a rip saw before planing. Plane the edge smooth, straight, square, and to the gauge line. Test with a try square from the face side.

4. *Plane to thickness*. With the marking gauge set to the required thickness, scribe a line on both edges and both

Scribe here all the way round

Fig. 7:27 Scribing to Thickness

ends (Figure 7:27). Be sure to scribe from the face side. Plane to this scribed line, and test for flatness and smoothness in the same manner as for the face side.

5. *Square one end.* Before measuring a piece of stock to its correct length, check one end to see that it is square with the face side and the face edge, and that it is straight and smooth. If this is not the case, it should be planed. Care must be taken when planing end grain or it will splinter at the edge. There are three methods of avoiding this splintering:

(a) A scrap piece of wood may be placed at the edge as shown in Figure 7:28.

(b) Plane halfway across the piece from each edge. This will prevent the edge from splitting if the plane is lifted slightly before the blade passes over the far edge. Test the end from the face side and edge.

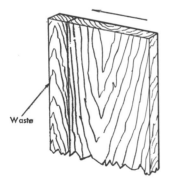

Fig. 7:28   Scrap Wood Placed at the Edge

Fig. 7:29   Planing Halfway from Each Edge

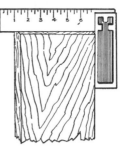

Fig. 7:30   End should be square with face edge.

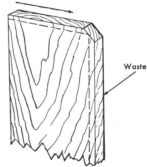

Fig. 7:31   Chamfer Cut on Waste Edge

(c) Cut a chamfer on the waste edge of the board and plane towards the chamfer (see Figure 7:31). If this method is used the end must be squared before the stock is reduced to the finished width.

6. *Measure and cut to length.* Mark the board to the exact length by measuring the desired distance from the finished end. Square a line across the piece to this point. Either plane or saw the piece

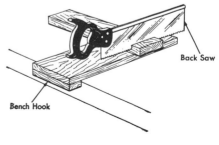

Fig. 7:32

45

to this line. If more than ¼″ is to be removed, it should be sawn with a back saw and a bench hook, as shown in Figure 7:32. Cut on the waste side of the line and lightly plane, using one of the methods just described for planing end grain.

This may appear to be a lengthy procedure to bring one piece of stock to the correct size and shape. However, you will find that you will save time in the long run by having pieces that fit properly. You will also gain valuable experience by performing these operations correctly.

In some cases when curves or special shapes must be cut from a pattern or layout, some of the steps just described here may be omitted and others substituted.

ASSIGNMENT

Planes and planing

1. List four types of bench planes. Give their purpose and their size.
2. Make a drawing of a jack plane and name the parts.
3. Explain why it is better to use a jointer plane to straighten the edge of a long piece of stock rather than a smoothing plane.
4. What is the special purpose of (a) a rabbet plane; (b) a router plane?
5. Show by arrows the direction in which the spokeshave should be pushed to smooth the curved edge

of the piece of stock shown here.
6. What type of plane would be used to plane surfaces A, B, C, and D in the piece of stock shown here?

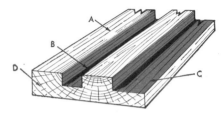

7. Illustrate by a sketch (a) an arris, (b) a chamfer and (c) a bevel.

Squaring stock

8. What is meant by "squaring stock"?
9. List the first three steps in the operation of squaring stock.
10. How should the face side of a board be tested to make certain that it is true?
11. Describe three methods of planing the end grain of a piece of stock.
12. Explain how a piece of stock is tested for wind.
13. Must the steps in squaring stock always be performed in the same order? If not, what other order could be suggested?

hand saws and their uses

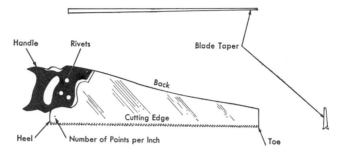

Fig. 8:1

Hand saws, which are so necessary for the cutting and shaping of wood and appear so easy to use, are, nevertheless, probably the most misused of all tools. Why is this so? Lack of knowledge about the proper way to use hand saws and inexperience account for much of the mistreatment of these tools. Below are some of the common ways in which they are incorrectly used and abused.

(a) The wrong type of saw is often used for the cut required.

(b) The wood being cut is not firmly held or supported.

(c) Cuts are made freehand without the use of proper layout lines.

(d) Hand saws are used that are not sharp.

(e) Inexperience and overconfidence result in a poor job; hand sawing requires more skill than is at first apparent.

In order to avoid these mistakes, you should become familiar with the various kinds of saws, their construction and their uses.

The essential parts of the hand saw are shown in Figure 8:1.

There are many types, sizes, and shapes of hand saws, each manufactured for a different purpose. The term *hand saw* usually refers to the general-purpose *cross-cut* or *rip saw* shown in Figure 8:1.

A number stamped on most saw blades near the heel indicates the number of points per inch. There is always one tooth less than there are points for each inch of saw blade, as is illustrated in Figure 8:2.

Cross-cut saws vary in coarseness from 7 points to 13 points per inch. Rip saws as a rule are somewhat coarser and may have as few as 5½ points per inch.

Hand saws are ground so that the

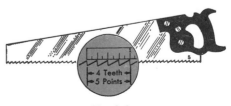

Fig. 8:2

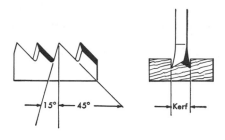

Fig. 8:3

blade tapers along the back from the handle to the toe and from the cutting edge to the back. This double taper of the blade makes the saw lighter to handle, stiffens the blade to prevent bending or buckling, and as well provides clearance for the saw blade as it cuts into the wood so that it will be less likely to bind or pinch.

Cross-cut saw

The purpose of this saw is to cut at a right angle to the grain of the wood. The teeth are so shaped that they cut the fibres evenly and smoothly. The shape of the teeth is shown in Figure 8:3.

So that the saw blade will have additional clearance to prevent it from binding, every other tooth is bent outward in the opposite direction. This is called the *set* of the saw. The amount of the set of a saw determines the width of the cut (*kerf*) the saw will

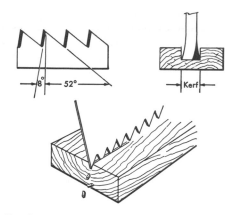

Fig. 8:4   Cutting Action of a Rip Saw

make. In general, coarse saws that are used for heavy work have more set than fine saws that may be used for lighter and finer work.

The length of a hand saw blade may vary from 20" to 28", the most used lengths being 24" and 26".

Rip saw

The rip saw is used to cut parallel to the grain of the wood. It differs from the cross-cut saw only in the shape of the teeth, which are like a series of chisels. Figure 8:4 illustrates the shape of the teeth and their cutting action through the fibres.

Although rip saws and cross-cut saws are made in identical sizes, the cross-cut saw is better adapted for

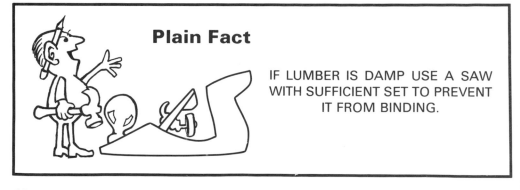

Plain Fact

IF LUMBER IS DAMP USE A SAW WITH SUFFICIENT SET TO PREVENT IT FROM BINDING.

general work because it can be used not only for cross-cutting but also for cutting diagonally across the grain, and, if necessary, for ripping when a fine cut is required, although in this case it cuts more slowly than the rip saw.

Back saw

The back saw, with 12 to 14 points per inch, is a fine cross-cut saw that is used for fine work. It generally has little set.

The blade has a stiffening rib at the back that holds the blade firm and tends to make it easier to make a straight and square cut. The common length of these saws is from 12" to 16". Such a saw is shown in Figure 7:32.

Coping saw

The coping saw, sometimes referred to as a *fret saw*, is used for making curved cuts in thin stock. The blade is held tight by the tension placed on it by the steel frame. The blades are narrow and are held in place by either a loop or a pin in the ends of the blade, which fits into the frame and handle.

When you use a coping saw, the work must be held firmly in a vise. If the work is thin, a piece of stock should be placed behind the wood being cut in order to stiffen it. A V block is often used when cutting small layouts, as shown in Figure 8:5. When inside designs are cut, a hole must be bored in the waste stock so that the blade can be inserted and the saw reassembled to cut out the design.

Compass saw

As the name implies, the compass saw was designed to cut circles. The blade is ground to a point at the end and with the back thinner than the cutting edge. This gives the blade clearance when cutting a sharp radius. This saw can be used for cutting with the grain or across it.

Keyhole saw

The keyhole saw is similar to the compass saw; in fact, they are often confused, so that the name keyhole saw is frequently used for both of these saws. However, the properly named keyhole saw, as shown in Figure 8:7, is smaller and is used for cutting smaller arcs. The blade is made so that it will slide into the handle in order for it to be used in more restricted areas. This saw is sometimes called a *pad saw*.

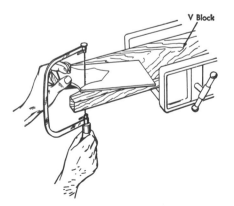

Fig. 8:6   Compass Saw

Fig. 8:5   When using a coping saw, cut on the down stroke.

Fig. 8:7   Keyhole Saw

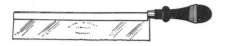

Fig. 8:8   Dovetail Saw Used for Fine Work on Thin Stock

How to use a hand saw

Since the use of a hand saw is so essential in woodwork, it is very important that you not only be familiar with the various types of hand saws but also that you learn how to use them correctly. To be proficient in woodwork, you must be able to square the end of a board with a hand saw so that the cut is perfectly square with the face side and the face edge, and so that the cut is made on the waste edge of the line.

Only through practice can one acquire the ability to use a hand saw skilfully. However, here are some pointers that may make your practice more effective:

Fig. 8:10   Rip Sawing

1. Make sure the work is held firmly. If the piece is short, it should be placed in a vise or on a bench hook. If the stock is long, it can be placed on two saw-horses. Hold the board steady with the knee (see Figure 8:9).

2. Use the correct saw for the job you are doing.

3. Start the saw kerf on the waste edge of the line by drawing the saw lightly over the edge of the board at the correct angle (see Figure 8:11).

James C. Fish Photography

Fig. 8:9   Cross-cutting

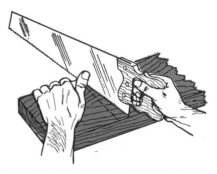

Fig. 8:11   Starting the Cut on the Waste Side of the Line

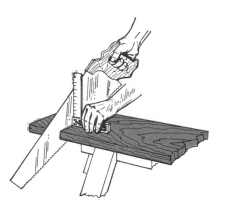

4. Hold the saw so that the blade is at right angles to the face of the board. It may be necessary at first to test the blade with a try square, as shown in Figure 8:12. However, with practice, you will be able to hold the saw automatically at the correct angle.

5. Finish the saw cut with short, easy strokes. To prevent the wood from splitting or breaking unevenly from its own weight, support the part to be cut off with the left hand.

Fig. 8:12 Testing the Saw for Vertical Position

James C. Fish Photography

Fig. 8:13 Use double layout lines when cutting plywood.

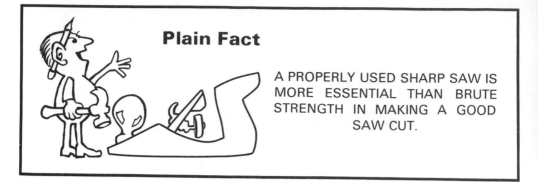

Plain Fact

A PROPERLY USED SHARP SAW IS MORE ESSENTIAL THAN BRUTE STRENGTH IN MAKING A GOOD SAW CUT.

6. Always cut to a line, never free-hand.

7. When cutting plywood sheet stock, use a cross-cut saw that is 10 points or finer. Work carefully, with the sheet well supported to prevent splintering on the under side. It helps if the pencil line is scored with a knife or chisel before cutting. This will prevent the fibres from being torn. When several pieces are to be cut from one sheet, it is a good idea to make double layout lines to indicate the edge of the saw kerf, as shown in Figure 8:13.

8. Hand saws are very useful tools; take proper care of them. Keep them sharp. Do not drop them or handle the blade with perspiring hands. Oil the blade occasionally to prevent rust.

ASSIGNMENT

1. Show, by means of a drawing, the difference between the teeth of a cross-cut saw and those of a rip saw. Show the angle of the teeth.
2. What does the number 10 stamped on the heel of a hand saw indicate?

3. What determines the width of a saw kerf?
4. What is meant by the set of a hand saw? Why must a hand saw have set?
5. Are there more or fewer points than teeth per inch on a hand saw?
6. Explain how you finish the cut when using a cross-cut hand saw.
7. What is the special purpose of (a) the back saw; (b) the coping saw; and (c) the compass saw?
8. Make a drawing of a hand saw and name the parts.
9. Where should the saw kerf be in relation to the line?
10. What two factors will help you master the skill of making a perfectly square cut with a hand saw?
11. State three rules for the care of a hand saw.
12. In what order would you make the cuts required to produce the piece shown here? Name the type of saw you would use for each cut.

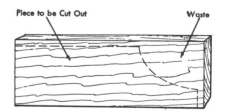

Piece to be Cut Out   Waste

braces, bits, and drills

Boring holes is often necessary in woodwork. It is a comparatively simple operation to perform, and if care is taken and a few precautions are followed, it should present no difficulty. Holes must be located accurately; they must be bored at the correct angle; and the wood should not be allowed to split when the bit comes through the back of the stock. The bits should be sharp.

The correct term for using a brace and bit is *boring a hole*. However, when a hand drill and a straight-shanked twist bit are used it is referred to as *drilling a hole*.

Brace

The tool shown in Figure 9:1 is a *brace*, not a *brace and bit* as it is sometimes incorrectly called. Any one of several types of bits may be attached to the brace to bore a hole.

The brace and an auger bit are used to bore holes ¼" and larger. The bit is securely attached to the brace by a chuck. Most braces are equipped with a

ratchet arrangement that allows the crank to turn independently of the chuck. This is a great help in boring holes in corners or restricted areas.

The size of a brace is determined by the size of the *sweep* (diameter of swing of the handle). They range in size from 8" to 14", with 10" the most popular size. The larger the sweep the greater the leverage. For boring large holes in hardwood it is better to use a brace with a large sweep.

Types of bits

Many types of bits are manufactured for boring holes, each for a special purpose. Some of these bits are described below.

Auger bit

The auger bits are used for most boring operations. They range in size in $1/16$"s from ¼" to 1". The size is designated by a number stamped on the square tang indicating the diameter of the bit in $1/16$"s. A number 9 bit is $9/16$" in diameter. The wood is cut by the two spurs and the cutting lips. The shavings are removed by a spiral twist; some auger bits have a double twist.

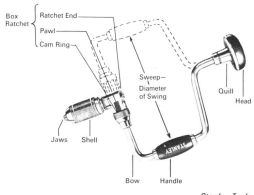

Box Ratchet — Ratchet End — Pawl — Cam Ring — Sweep— Diameter of Swing — Quill — Head — Jaws — Shell — Bow — Handle

Stanley Tools

Fig. 9:1   Brace

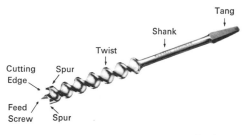

Tang — Shank — Twist — Cutting Edge — Spur — Feed Screw — Spur

Stanley Tools

Fig. 9:2   Auger Bit

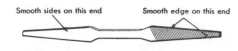

Fig. 9:3   Bit File

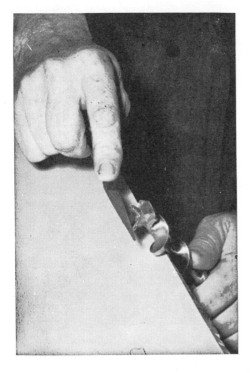

Fig. 9:4   Sharpening the Spurs

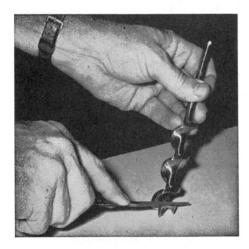

Fig. 9:5   Sharpening the Cutting Lips

For best results the bit must be sharp. An auger bit file should be used for this purpose (see Figure 9:3). File the spurs on the inside (Figure 9:4) and the cutting lips on the upper side, as shown in Figure 9:5. You should obtain special instructions before attempting to sharpen an auger bit as it is very easy to spoil the bit.

Expansive bits

For holes larger than 1" or for holes with dimensions other than even $1/16$" s, e.g., $25/32$", an *expansive bit* should be used (Figure 9:6). The adjustable part of this bit is the sliding cutting bar that can be slid in or out by loosening a set screw or by using a dial arrangement, as shown in Figure 9:6 B. The cutter bar is graduated in $1/16$" s for easy setting. Most expansive bits have two cutting bars that can be used to give the bit a wider range of size. There are two common sizes of expansive bits: one with a capacity of ½" to 1½", the other of ⅞" to 3". These bits have a feed screw with fine threads, for when a large hole is being bored, the bit should be drawn into the wood slowly. It is difficult to bore a deep hole with this type of bit.

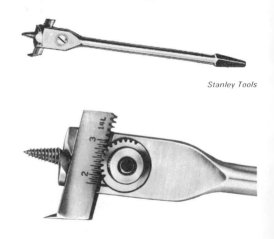

Stanley Tools

The Irwin Auger Bit Company

Fig. 9:6   Two Types of Expansive Bit

Wadkin

Fig. 9:7   Forstner Bit

Fig. 9:10   Rose Bud Countersink

Forstner bits

A Forstner bit (Figure 9:7) is often used for holes that do not go all the way through the piece and require a flat bottom. Since the cutting spur runs all the way round the bit, it has less tendency to split out the wood on the far side of the piece. This fact accounts for its use in boring holes in plywoods, which tend to split out much more easily than solid wood. Since the Forstner bit has no feed screw either to locate it on a definite point or to draw it into the wood, it is more often used in a drill press than in a brace. However, it can be used with either.

Steel twist bit or drill

The twist bits for wood are similar to those used for metal cutting except that they may be ground to a sharper cutting angle and are often made from a milder steel. The small sizes, which range from 1/16" to 1/4", have round shanks and are generally used in a hand drill. The larger sizes, from 1/4" to 1/2", may have square shanks and are used with a brace. The small twist bits are often used for clearance or pilot holes for wood screws. (See Figure 9:8.)

Gimlet bit

The gimlet bit (Figure 9:9) is also used for pilot holes for wood screws. It is made with a long taper that corresponds to the taper of a wood screw.

Boring holes with a brace and bit

Most holes should be bored at a right angle to the surface. This is often a difficult operation. You will find it a big help if you check the direction of the bit with a try square, as shown in Figure 9:11. Check the bit in two directions. You may get another person to stand back and sight the bit as you start the hole. Make sure you have the bit in a perpendicular position as you start to bore. Do not attempt to change the direction after the bit has entered the wood as the bit may be bent. After some experience at boring holes you will be able to hold the bit automatically in an upright position without the aid of the try square.

May have a round or square shank

Fig. 9:8   Twist Bit or Drill

Fig. 9:9   Gimlet Bit

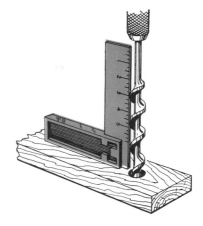

Fig. 9:11   Testing the Bit for Upright Position

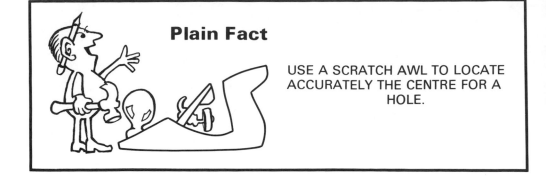

Plain Fact

USE A SCRATCH AWL TO LOCATE
ACCURATELY THE CENTRE FOR A
HOLE.

If the hole is to be bored at an angle other than a right angle, a sliding T-bevel is useful for checking the accuracy of the angle (see Figure 9:12).

If the hole is to be bored all the way through the material, care must be taken not to splinter the wood when the bit breaks through the piece. This can be avoided by boring from one side of the piece until the screw point comes through. Then finish boring the hole from the reverse side. Another method is to clamp a scrap piece to the back of the stock. Figures 9:13 to 9:15 illustrate these points.

When the hole does not go all the way through, a depth gauge should be

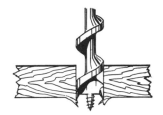

Fig. 9:13   Do not let this happen.

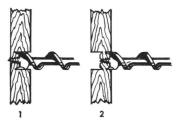

Fig. 9:14   Boring from Both Sides of the Material

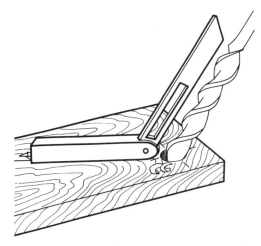

Fig. 9:12   Testing the Bit for Desired Angle

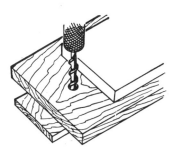

Fig. 9:15   Protecting the Back of the Work by Using a Scrap Piece of Wood Behind It

used. An adjustable depth gauge is shown in Figure 9:16. If one of these gauges is not available, a wood block may be bored and used as shown in Figure 9:17. For accurate location of the hole a scratch awl should be used to make a punch mark.

Hand drills

For boring small holes up to ¼″ it is often faster and easier to use a hand drill (Figure 9:18). Only straight-shanked drills can be used with this tool. If the holes need to be a definite depth, a block of wood can be drilled and used as a depth gauge in the same manner as was illustrated in Figure 9:17.

Hand drills are relatively easy to use because they are used only for drilling small holes (generally ¼″ or less). However, care should be taken to locate the position of the hole properly with a

Stanley Tools

Fig. 9:16   Depth Gauge

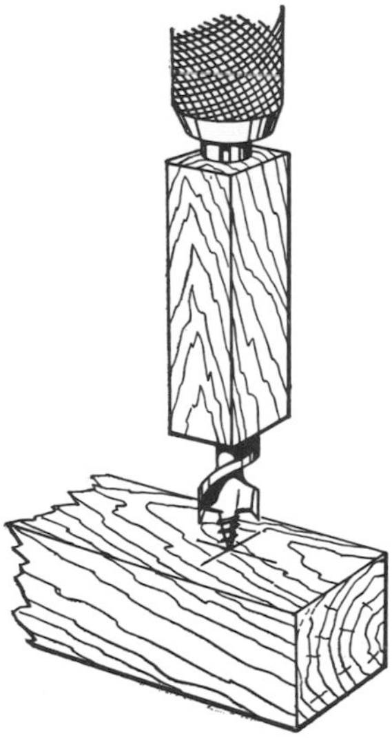

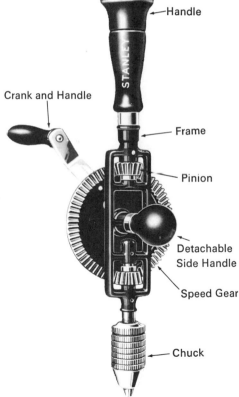

Handle

Crank and Handle

Frame

Pinion

Detachable
Side Handle

Speed Gear

Chuck

Stanley Tools

Fig. 9:18   Hand Drill

Fig. 9:17   Wood Block Depth Gauge

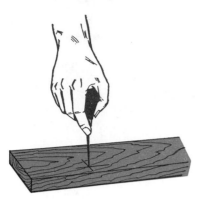

Fig. 9:19   Locating the Hole with a Scratch Awl

Millers Falls Co.

Fig. 9:21   Breast Drill

Fig. 9:20   Hold the drill steady in a perpendicular position.

Stanley Tools

Fig. 9:22   Push-pull Drill

scratch awl (Figure 9:19). Hold the drill straight and at a right angle to the face of the work (Figure 9:20). Do not allow the drill to wobble while you turn the crank. This tends to make the hole oversized and may break the drill.

A breast drill is used for drilling larger holes in wood with straight-shanked twist bits up to ½″ in diameter. It is also used occasionally for drilling holes in metal. A breast drill is shown in Figure 9:21.

The automatic push-pull type of drill is a handy tool for boring screw holes when installing hardware. It is also useful for boring holes for nails where there is danger of the wood splitting. It is a rapid-action tool that can be used

in a restricted area. Special bits must be used; they have two straight flutes and range in size from $1/16″$ to $3/16″$. An automatic drill and bit is shown in Figure 9:22.

ASSIGNMENT

1. What precautions should be observed when boring a hole in wood?
2. What are the purposes of the following parts of a brace? (a) jaws (b) ratchet
3. How is the size of a brace determined?
4. State two uses of (a) an expansive bit and (b) a Forstner bit.

5. Make a sketch of an auger bit and name the parts.
6. What would be the sizes of auger bits that have the following numbers stamped on the shank: 6, 12, and 16?
7. Explain how an auger bit is sharpened.
8. Why should the hole be located with a scratch awl?
9. What method can you use as an aid in boring a hole perpendicular to the surface?
10. List two methods of boring a hole through a board without splintering the back.
11. (a) When is a depth gauge used? (b) What can be used instead of a depth gauge?
12. (a) For what operation would you use a hand drill rather than a brace and bit? (b) What types of bits are used in a hand drill?
13. For what type of work is the automatic push-pull drill used?
14. What type of bit would you use to bore a hole $25/32$" in diameter?

hammers and nails

Claw hammers

The tool used for driving nails is the claw hammer, shown in Figure 10:1. It is so named because of the claw shape of the forged head. The claws add weight and balance to the hammer, but their main purpose is for drawing nails. Hammers are made with either a curved claw or a ripping (straight) claw. To prevent the wood from being damaged on the last blow when driving a nail, the driving face of the hammer is slightly rounded.

The size of a hammer is determined by the weight of the head, which may range from 6 to 20 ounces. The 12-ounce is the most popular light-weight hammer, while the 16-ounce is the one most used by carpenters. Good hammers are forged from a high grade of steel, and are carefully heat-treated to produce a very hard-wearing finish on the striking surface. The metal in the claws is treated to make them tough but more elastic than the head which allows nails to be drawn without danger of the claws breaking.

Most hammer handles are made from second-growth hickory because this wood is strong and tough. Hickory also has a certain amount of spring, which is necessary for the easy driving of nails. The handle is fitted snugly into the adze eye and secured there by driving metal or wooden wedges into the end of the handle, as shown in Figure 10:2.

Some of the newer types of hammers have unbreakable handles. The head and the handle is a single forged metal part, while the handle grip is made of leather or neoprene, such as that of the hammer shown in Figure 10:3. These hammers have one disadvantage in that there is no spring to the solid metal handle. This is most noticeable when driving a number of spikes, for the wrist becomes tired more quickly.

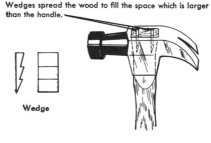

Wedges spread the wood to fill the space which is larger than the handle.

Wedge

Fig. 10:2

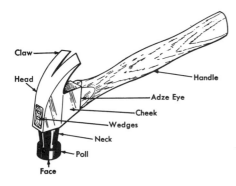

Fig. 10:1 Claw Hammer

Fig. 10:3 Unbreakable Hammer

Fig. 10:5   Face Nailing

Fig. 10:4   Block Used for Leverage When Drawing a Nail

Fig. 10:6   Toe Nailing

Use of the hammer

Although the hammer is one of the most common tools, it is often misused. It should be held at the end of the handle for easy and accurate nailing. (Do not "choke" the hammer.) The face of the hammer head should be kept free of oil, paint, glue, or other material. If this is not done, the striking power is reduced, often causing the hammer to glance off the nail and bend it or to damage the wood. The hammer head can be kept clean by rubbing it with sandpaper or emery cloth.

When you are drawing a nail with a claw hammer, a block of wood should be placed under the claw as shown in Figure 10:4. This protects the wood and provides more leverage. If the nail is a large one, a second block may be required after the nail has been partially withdrawn. The additional leverage gained will make the work much easier and may prevent the handle from breaking.

There are two general methods of nailing: *face nailing* and *toe nailing*. Most nails are driven at approximately 90° to the surface. This is called face nailing, and is illustrated in Figure 10:5. Where the end of a piece meets a flat

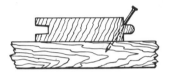

Fig. 10:7   Edge Nailing

surface of another it is often necessary to toe nail the two members together, as in Figure 10:6. Carpenters often use this method when building frame houses. Matched lumber such as tongue-and-groove flooring is generally held in place by *edge nailing*, as shown in Figure 10:7.

To prevent splitting, nails should not be driven too close to the edge or end of a board. Staggering the nails, rather than driving them in line with the grain, is a good idea. Drive nails with care and accuracy. Hammer marks on the face of the wood indicate that the job was done by an unskilled person.

Nail set

If you wish to conceal the nails, a *nail set* should be used. (This tool should not be referred to as a punch.) The specific purpose of a nail set is to drive the nail head below the surface of the wood, so that the hole can then be

Plain Fact

DO NOT USE LARGER NAILS THAN ARE NECESSARY TO DO THE JOB.

filled and made almost invisible. Colour-coated panel nails are now being manufactured that resemble very closely the colour of popular prefinished plywoods and wallboards. These nails are driven flush with the surface of the wallboard, thus eliminating the need for setting the nails and filling the holes in the panelling.

Most nail sets are from 4″ to 5″ long, with a knurled centre part tapered to a point. The point is cup-shaped to prevent it from sliding off the nail head. There are various point sizes ranging from $^1/_{32}$″ to $^5/_{32}$″. The nail set used should have a point slightly smaller than the head of the finishing nail being set.

Fig. 10:8 Using a Nail Set

Ripping bar

For drawing spikes, or even smaller nails, from hard wood a *ripping bar* should be used. This tool is often called a *pinch bar* or *wrecking bar*. The greater leverage provided by this bar makes the job much easier.

Nails

For centuries the most common method of fastening wood has been by means of nails. Nails are now such a familiar household article that it is difficult for us to realize that they were once scarce and difficult to obtain. The first nails

Fig. 10:9 Ripping Bar

were forged by hand. There are records of metal nails being used as long ago as 1100 B.C., but it was not until 1777 that a machine was invented to manufacture nails. These nails were stamped out of sheet stock and were called *cut nails* (see Figure 10:11). This type of nail is still being used. In 1835 the first machine to make nails from wire was invented. This ushered in the era of the wire nail as we know it today. Many improvements have since been made in nail manufacture and the production speeded up so that they are now made at reasonable cost. Wire is fed into an automatic machine at a high speed, and in one operation the head and the point are formed and the nail ejected to make way for the next. In this way the machines are capable of producing more than five hundred nails per minute.

Most nails are made from steel. However, some are manufactured from brass, copper, and aluminum. These nails are softer and bend more easily than steel nails. They are also more expensive, but do not rust as readily. For this reason they are often used for boat building or whenever there is danger of corrosion.

Nails are made in a great many sizes and shapes for various purposes. Five of the most-used types are shown in Figure 10:10.

Common nails are the general-purpose nails used for structural or other heavy work where the nail heads may be exposed. Common nails over 4" in length are usually referred to as spikes but are catalogued as common nails.

Finishing nails, as the name implies, are used for finishing work where the nail heads should not be exposed. They are generally set below the surface and the hole filled with a wood filler. Finishing nails less than 1" long are called *brads*.

Flooring nails have a tapered head that will better fit at the tongue of the flooring board.

Roofing nails have a large flat head. They are used on rolled-type roofing materials and are available in various

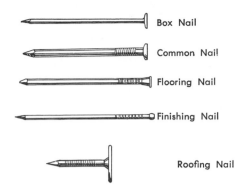

Fig. 10:10 Types of Nails

lengths from ¾" to 1½". A variation of these nails is the *shingle nail*, which is somewhat lighter with a smaller head. These are used for wood or asphalt shingles. Roofing nails are often coated with zinc, or galvanized to make them rust resistant.

Box nails are similar to common nails but are made from a lighter-gauge wire. They are often coated with a rosin cement, which gives them more holding power. These nails are used mainly for crating and packing boxes.

Nails are now being manufactured with small barbs that dig into the wood to increase their holding power. *Twist* or *spiral* nails are used extensively in building construction. The twisted shank of these nails causes them to thread themselves into the wood as they are driven, thus increasing their holding power. A 2½" spiral common nail is made from lighter wire than the ordinary 2½" common nail. For this reason, spiral nails do not split the wood as easily as the conventional nail.

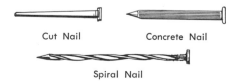

Fig. 10:11 Special Nails

Fig. 10:12 Sectional View of Deformed Swedish Nails

There are also more nails to the pound. Spiral nails are not twisted as they are made, but are manufactured from wire that has already been twisted.

The holding power of nails depends to a large extent on the friction of the wood fibres on the surface of the nail. The nail displaces and compresses the wood fibres as it is driven. The tendency of the fibres to spring back into their original position creates friction, which holds the nail. With this principle in mind, nails are now being made with the largest possible outside area without increasing the gauge or wire size. A sectional view of some of these nails is shown in Figure 10:12. These nails are commonly called *Swedish nails* because of their origin.

Concrete nails (Figure 10:11) are extensively used in building construction for nailing wood members to masonry walls. They have been heat-treated to make the metal very hard and thus prevent them from bending. These nails are thicker than the corresponding length of common nail. They are serrated for the full length of the nail to provide more holding power. Although they will not bend easily, they have a tendency to break and fly back while being driven. Safety glasses should be worn when you are driving concrete nails.

Nails are specified by their length, metal, use, and type. They are also referred to by their *penny size*, abbreviated to the letter *d* after the number, e.g., 6 d, 7 d, and 8 d. The term "penny" is an old English one and referred to the weight of 1000 nails, e.g., 1

thousand 8 d nails weighed 8 pounds. The chart below lists the penny size and corresponding length and gauge for common nails today.

Penny Size	Length in Inches	Wire Gauge Size	Approx. No. per lb.
2 d	1	15	876
3 d	1¼	14	568
4 d	1½	12½	316
5 d	1¾	12½	271
6 d	2	11½	181
7 d	2¼	11½	161
8 d	2½	10¼	106
9 d	2¾	10¼	96
10 d	3	9	69
12 d	3¼	8	63
16 d	3½	7	49
20 d	4	6	31
30 d	4½	5	24
40 d	5	4	18
50 d	5½	3	14
60 d	6	2	11

Signode Corporation

Fig. 10:13 Automatic Nailing Machine

Even the simple operation of driving nails has now been automated. There are several types of automatic nailing devices on the market that are extensively used in building construction and in factories. These range from the spring-operated stapler, used for such jobs as fastening insulation material or ceiling tile in homes, to the heavy compressed-air-operated gun nailers that will drive nails up to 3″ in length. These guns are easily loaded by inserting strips of nails or staples into the magazine cartridge. They are simple to operate and relatively inexpensive, and save time when large quantities of nails are to be driven. Figure 10:13 illustrates one type of automatic nailing machine. There are many other sizes and types in use and still others are being developed.

ASSIGNMENT

Hammers

1. (a) How is the size of a claw hammer determined? (b) Which size is most used by carpenters?
2. Make a drawing of a claw hammer and name the parts.
3. How is the hammer head secured to a wooden handle?
4. What advantage does a wooden hammer handle have over a metal one?
5. (a) Why should the head of a hammer be kept clean? (b) How can it be cleaned?
6. How can you secure more leverage when pulling nails?
7. Describe two methods of nailing.
8. What is meant by "staggering the nails"?
9. How and why are nail sets used?
10. What is the advantage of using a ripping bar rather than a claw hammer for drawing nails?

Nails

11. What are the advantages and disadvantages of copper nails?
12. Make a drawing of four of the most used types of nails. State the use of each.
13. When should pilot holes be drilled for nails?
14. Why are galvanized nails used?
15. How do box nails differ from common nails?
16. What is the advantage of the spiral nail?
17. Explain why the Swedish-type nail should have a greater holding power than the conventional round nail of the same gauge.
18. In what way do concrete nails differ from common nails?
19. Explain how the wood fibres provide the holding power for the nails.
20. When ordering nails, how do you specify what you want?

CHAPTER ELEVEN

chisels

The operation of shaping and forming wood by hand is performed largely with a saw or a chisel. Of these two hand tools, the chisel requires the greater skill, and care should be taken to select the correct type for the work being done.

The principal parts of a chisel are the handle and the blade. The latter is generally made of well-tempered tool steel. The blades vary in width by sixteenths of an inch from ⅛" to 1", and from 1" to 2" in one-quarter-inch sizes. The blades range in length from 3" to 8".

The face of the chisel is flat. The bevel for the cutting edge is ground on the back and at a right angle to the edge. The edges of most chisels are also bevelled to make them lighter and easier to use in a restricted area. The turned handles are generally made from hickory or boxwood. However, some chisels have moulded plastic handles.

There are two general types of wood chisels, the *tang chisel* and the *socket chisel*. They are distinguished by the way they are made and the purpose for which they are used. Figure 11:1 shows a tang chisel. It is used for light work and is also referred to as a *paring chisel*. The operation of paring consists of removing thin shavings with a cutting tool. Paring chisels should be used only with hand pressure. So that they

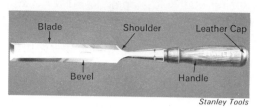

Fig. 11:2   Socket Chisel

will have most of the weight at the lower end for better handling, they have only a light, pointed prong or tang that fits up into the handle. To prevent the handle from splitting, a shoulder is forged on the blade near the shank. A light brass ferrule protects the handle at this point.

Socket chisels are more sturdily built to make them suitable for heavier work. They are generally used with a mallet for a type of work called mortising, hence the term, *mortising chisel*. The blade of a socket chisel tapers from the cutting edge to the end where it is socket-shaped to receive the handle (see Figure 11:2). The end of the handle is reinforced with a leather cap to cushion the blows of the mallet and to prevent the handle from splitting.

There are many variations of both these types of chisels. The *firmer chisel* is a medium-weight chisel for general work. The *butt chisel* has a short blade and is used for accurate work. It is often used for setting in hinges. *Gouges* (Figure 11:3) have half-round or curved cutting edges for cutting special shapes. They may be ground from the inside or the outside. *Carving tools* are generally made in sets. They are small, specially shaped chisels used almost exclusively for wood carving. These chisels may be of either the socket or the tang type.

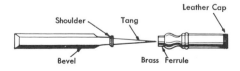

Fig. 11:1   Tang Chisel

Plain Fact

THERE IS LESS CHANCE OF CUT-
TING YOURSELF WHEN WORKING
WITH A SHARP CHISEL THAN WITH
A DULL ONE.

Fig. 11:3 Gouges

Fig. 11:4 Chisel with Steel Cap

A serviceable type of chisel is illustrated in Figure 11:4. The tang is attached to the steel cap, which will
withstand hammer blows. It has a hard
plastic handle.

How to use a chisel

The best way to learn to do neat and
accurate work with a chisel is through
practice.

Chiselling may be done horizontally
or vertically. In either case, it is necessary to hold the wood securely in a vise
or with a clamp. Make sure the chisel
is sharp.

For horizontal chiselling, push the
chisel with one hand and use the other
hand as a guide and brake. Keep the
bevel of the cutting edge facing up (see

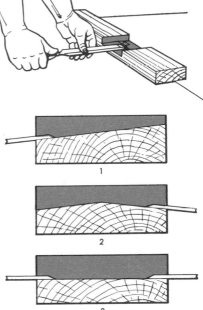

Fig. 11:5 Horizontal Chiselling

Figure 11:5). If cutting across the grain,
chisel from both edges to avoid splintering the edge grain (see Figure 11:5,
part 3). When cutting parallel with the
grain, a smoother cut can be made by
holding the chisel on an angle to the
work so that the chisel makes a shearing cut.

Vertical chiselling generally requires
more pressure on the chisel. This can

best be accomplished by placing the left hand over the blade, as shown in Figure 11:6.

When chiselling vertically or mortising, a mallet is often required (see Figure 11:7).

When cutting end grain, tilt the chisel and use it like a knife, as shown in Figure 11:8.

Stanley Tools

Fig. 11:8   Cutting End Grain

Stanley Tools

Fig. 11:6   Vertical Chiselling

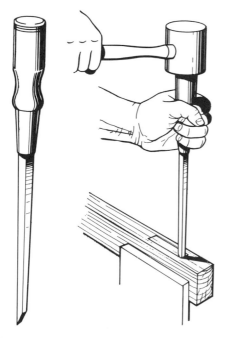

Fig. 11:7   Cutting Out a Mortise

ASSIGNMENT

1. Which surface of the chisel is bevelled, the face or the back?
2. (a) What are the two main types of chisel? (b) How are these types distinguished?
3. What is meant by (a) paring? (b) mortising?
4. Show by means of a sketch the difference between a tang chisel and a socket chisel.
5. What is the purpose of the leather cap at the end of the handle on a socket chisel?
6. List four special types of chisel and state the purpose of each.
7. List two types of gouge chisel.
8. List the procedures you should follow when using a chisel vertically.
9. What is meant by a "shearing cut"?
10. Make a list of several woodworking operations that require the use of a chisel. State which type of chisel you think should be used for each.

wood screws and screwdrivers

Wood screws are the most versatile of all fasteners because they can be used for so many purposes, such as fastening wood to wood, fastening metal to wood, or attaching all types of hardware and other metal fittings to a wood surface. They have a greater holding power than nails and enable a project to be dismantled at any time without damage to the surrounding wood.

Wood screw specifications

Different types of wood screws have different distinguishing features or "specifications". Some of these are indicated below. It is necessary to refer to each of them when ordering wood screws.

(a) Metal

Wood screws for most uses are made of steel; these are often called *brights* because of their shining appearance. Screws are also made from copper and from brass, both of which are more resistant to corrosion than steel.

(b) Size

The size of a wood screw is determined by its length in inches and the diameter of the shank just below the head. This diameter is given in the American screw gauge size. The screw gauge differs from the standard wire gauge in that the 0 size indicates the smallest size. As the gauge size increases, so does the diameter of the screw. This is the reverse of the standard wire gauge. Screws vary in gauge from 0 to 24 and in length from ¼" to 1" in steps of ⅛",

from 1" to 3" in steps of ¼", and from 3" to 5" in steps of ½".

(c) Shape of the head

Although there are many wood screws made with various-shaped heads for decorative or other purposes, the three most commonly used shapes are the flat, the oval, and the round (see Figure 12:1).

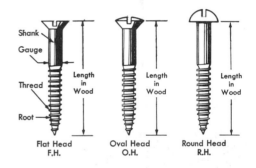

Fig. 12:1   Types of Screws

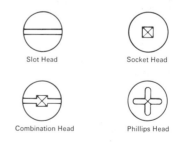

Fig. 12:2   Impressions in the Heads of Wood Screws

(d) Type of slot

The type of screwdriver used on wood screws depends on the shape of the recess in the head. Four of these are shown in Figure 12:2.

(e) Finish

Wood screws are made with various finishes. They may, for example, be chrome-plated, nickel-plated, galvanized, or blued.

(f) Quantity

Screws are sold by the box containing one gross (12 dozen).

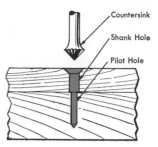

Although screws are superior to nails because of their holding power, they are more expensive and require more time and care if they are to be properly installed.

Fastening with wood screws requires the use of some or all of the following tools: hand drill, straight-shanked drill bits, scratch awl, countersink, and screwdriver. The correct size and shape of screwdriver must be used to fit the screw being driven.

Since screws are thicker than nails, they displace more wood when they are driven. This makes it necessary in most cases to bore clearance or shank holes through the first piece of wood. This hole should be the same size as the shank of the screw so that it is a smooth fit. The pilot, or anchor, hole in the second piece is smaller to allow

Fig. 12:3   Pilot Hole for Wood Screw

the threads of the screw to cut themselves firmly into the wood. If no pilot holes are bored, the screws may be too hard to turn or they may split the wood. In soft wood or end grain the pilot hole may be made with a scratch awl.

The table below shows the recommended shank and pilot hole sizes for the commoner gauge sizes of screw. The position of these holes is shown in Figure 12:3.

The sizes listed in the table may not always be the correct ones because of the variation in the hardness of woods. It is a good idea to do a little experimenting with a scrap piece of wood before boring the holes in the finished work. Screws will drive more easily into

Wood Screw Table

Gauge No.	4	5	6	7	8	9	10	11	12
Diam. of Shank Hole (inches)	$1/8$	$1/8$	$5/32$	$5/32$	$3/16$	$3/16$	$3/16$	$7/32$	$7/32$
Diam. of Pilot Hole (inches)	$3/32$	$3/32$	$1/8$	$1/8$	$5/32$	$5/32$	$5/32$	$5/32$	$5/32$

hard wood if a little soap is rubbed on them.

If flat-head screws are to be used, the top of the head should be set down flush with the surface of the wood. In Figure 12:3 a countersink, which is the tool used for this purpose, is shown.

How to fasten with screws

(a) Locate the position of the screw. Make a dent with a scratch awl at this point.

(b) Bore the correct size of clearance hole through the first piece. (See table on page 70 for correct size.) Use a straight-shanked drill bit in the hand drill or drill press.

(c) Place the first piece over the piece to be attached to it, and mark the location of the pilot hole with a scratch awl, as shown in Figure 12:4.

(d) Bore the pilot hole the correct diameter (see table). Care should be taken not to bore the hole too deep. It should be slightly shallower than the length of the screw.

(e) If necessary, countersink the hole for the screw head.

(f) Use a screwdriver that fits the slot of the screw snugly. Hold the screwdriver firmly and in line with the centre of the

Stanley Tools

Fig. 12:5   Screwdriver Bit

screw. This will tend to prevent it from slipping out of the slot. If the screw is hard to turn or the slot is becoming burred, the pilot hole may not be big enough or deep enough. Remove the screw and enlarge the pilot hole or put a little soap on the screw to serve as a lubricant. A brace and screwdriver bit may be used on large screws where more leverage is required (see Figure 12:5).

If screws are to be completely concealed, they may be set below the surface and plugged, as shown in Figure 12:6.

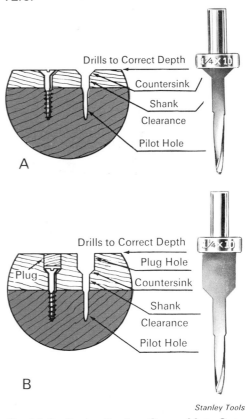

Drills to Correct Depth

Countersink

Shank

Clearance

Pilot Hole

A

Drills to Correct Depth

Plug Hole

Plug

Countersink

Shank

Clearance

Pilot Hole

B

Stanley Tools

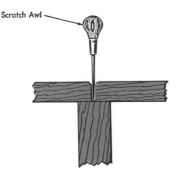

Scratch Awl

Fig. 12:4   Locating the Pilot Hole

Fig. 12:6   Boring Tools — Screw Mate Sets

When a large number of screws of the same size are to be used, much time can be saved by using a special boring tool that bores both the shank and pilot holes and countersinks the shank hole in one operation. Two of these boring tools are shown in Figure 12:6 (A and B). A different boring tool must be used for each length and gauge size of screw.

Screwdrivers

There are many sizes and types of screwdrivers. The standard straight screwdriver used for slotted screws is shown in Figure 12:7.

The length of blade varies from 2" to 18" in 1" intervals. They have either wood or plastic handles. For driving or removing screws in a restricted area the stubby, or close quarters, screwdrivers are used. These have both a short blade and a short handle with an over-all length of 2¾" (see Figure 12:8). An offset screwdriver may also be used for this purpose (see Figure 12:9).

Many screwdrivers are equipped with a ratchet arrangement allowing the handle to turn either to the right or to the left independently of the blade. The spiral automatic ratchet screwdriver is a labour- and time-saving tool that will drive or remove screws as the handle is moved up and down. Various sizes and shapes of tips can be used to fit all types of screws. Care must be taken when using this tool, as the blade can easily slip out of the screw slot on the downward stroke and damage the wood or the screw head. The automatic ratchet type is often referred to as the *Yankee screwdriver*.

Socket head and star head screwdrivers come in sets. The larger the screw, the larger the size of tip required. They are not repairable when they become worn. The straight screwdrivers, however, can be reground or

filed to shape. If the tip becomes rounded or bevelled, it tends to rise out of the slot and spoil the screw head and often damages the wood. Figure 12:11 shows a tip that requires grinding and one that is the correct shape. Note the difference.

In the trade, socket head screws are often referred to as *Robertson* screws and the screws with the star-shaped impression as *Phillips* screws because it was these companies that developed and manufactured them. However, they are now produced and sold by many

Stanley Tools

Fig. 12:7   Standard Screwdriver

Millers Falls Co.

Fig. 12:8   Stubby-Type Screwdriver

Millers Falls Co.

Fig. 12:9   Offset Screwdriver

Stanley Tools

Fig. 12:10 Automatic Ratchet Screwdriver

Plain Fact

TO PRODUCE NEAT WORK SCREW-
DRIVER TIPS MUST BE CORRECTLY
SHAPED TO FIT THE SCREW SLOT.

other companies and under other trade names. Socket-type wood screws are to a large extent replacing the slotted head screws in woodworking, especially in industry, because there is less chance of the screwdriver slipping and burring the head or damaging the wood. The socket head screwdriver point is more adaptable to an electric screwdriver. Slot screws, however, are still the most popular for domestic use.

Awls

Two aids for installing wood screws are the *brad awl* and the *scratch awl* which is slightly larger and heavier. Either tool may be used for properly marking the exact screw location. For small screws, such as those used for attaching hardware, the awl may be used to make the pilot hole. The point must be kept sharp.

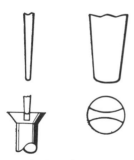

Improperly Shaped Screwdriver Tip.

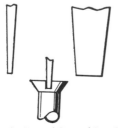

Properly Ground Screwdriver Tip.

Fig. 12:11

ASSIGNMENT

1. Why are screws superior to nails as fastening devices?
2. From what metal are wood screws manufactured?
3. How does the American screw gauge differ from the standard wire gauge?
4. How is the size of a wood screw determined?
5. What are the three shapes of screw heads?
6. Why are some screws coated with galvanizing?
7. How many screws are there in 6 gross?
8. When ordering screws, what specifications must you list?

9. What hand tools are generally used to insert wood screws?

10. Why is it necessary to bore a clearance hole in the first piece of wood?

11. How does a pilot hole differ from a clearance hole?

12. When is it unnecessary to bore a pilot hole?

13. Give the shank and pilot sizes required for a No. 8 and a No. 10 wood screw.

14. List the first four steps in installing screws in hard wood.

15. What should be done if the screw is too hard to turn?

16. What is the advantage of using (a) a ratchet screwdriver? (b) an automatic screwdriver?

17. What may happen if an improperly shaped screwdriver point is used?

18. What use is made of the scratch awl when fastening with wood screws?

19. If three wood screws are to be used to fasten together the two pieces of softwood shown here, show the location of the screws and state what size screws should be used.

glues and clamps

Wood glues and adhesives are not a development of modern times; in fact they were used by the Egyptians 3000 years ago. Some of the ancient Greek furniture that was assembled with glue is still intact in our museums. Since then there have been many advances in the manufacture of glue and many new types have been developed for specific purposes.

Wood glues may be classified according to their origin, their curing temperature, and their resistance to moisture.

(a) Origin. Glues may be made with a base of natural materials, such as animal or vegetable matter, or they may have a synthetic base, involving petroleum or chemicals.

(b) Curing Temperatures. Low-temperature-curing glues cure or harden at room temperature. Intermediate-temperature-curing glues will harden at temperatures of from 80° to 200°F. High-temperature-curing glues will harden only at temperatures in excess of 200°F. The heat must be artificially applied to the glue point for curing.

(c) Resistance to Moisture. Glues are divided into three groups: waterproof glues, moisture-resistant glues, dry bond or non-moisture-resistant glues.

Types of glue

Some of the types most frequently used are:

Prepared liquid animal glues
These are made from hides and bones of animals. They are brown in colour

and slow-setting. Being ready-prepared they are convenient to use, but they are not waterproof.

Hot glue
Animal glue is also made in a flake form. This must be soaked in water for twenty-four hours and then heated in a double boiler arrangement or an electric glue pot, and used as hot glue. It sets rapidly, making it necessary to lose no time in clamping the work after applying the glue. It is not waterproof.

Casein glue
This type, which comes in a powdered form, is made from skim milk and chemicals and needs only to be mixed with water. It must be used within a few hours after it is mixed and after mixing must *not* be placed in metal containers. It is white in colour, moisture resistant, and slow-setting.

Resin glue
Resin glue is probably the most commonly used of all glues for general purposes. A great deal of chemical research and experiment has gone into the development of the urea formaldehyde plastic resin glues now in use. *Liquid resin glue* has become very popular for industrial and household purposes because it is convenient to use in its ready-prepared form. It holds well, is water resistant, and what is probably most important of all, sets so rapidly that it is completely hard in one hour. This saves a great deal of clamping time. This glue is white but dries to an almost transparent film. *Resorcinol*

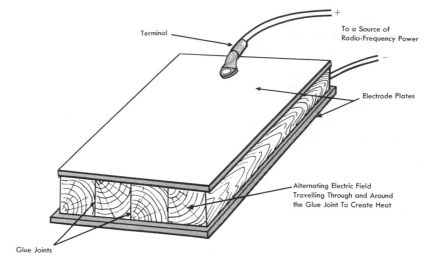

Terminal

To a Source of
Radio-Frequency Power

Electrode Plates

Alternating Electric Field
Travelling Through and Around
the Glue Joint To Create Heat

Glue Joints

Fig. 13:1   Dielectric Heating

resin glue is made in a powdered form that must be mixed with water before using. It is light brown but does not stain the wood. This glue is often used for boat building and for other work where waterproof glue is essential. The joints must be well fitted and clamped. Follow the manufacturer's instructions closely when mixing resin glues.

Fast-drying *thermosetting glues*, which require heat to harden, are now in general use in many woodworking industries. The glue is spread on the wood, which is then placed between two metal plates referred to as electrodes, and a source of high-frequency electric current is connected to terminals on the electrodes. The result of the current flow through the wood is to agitate the molecules that make up the wood. This molecular friction generates the heat within the wood necessary to cure or harden the glue rapidly. This process is extensively used for the manufacture of moulded plywood furniture and other wood products. Figures 13:1, 13:2, and 13:3 illustrate three methods of gluing wood using high-frequency electric current. This process

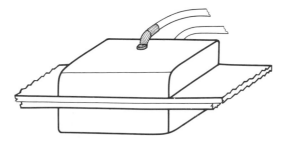

Fig. 13:2   Gluing Stock While It Is in Motion. Long thin members are passed between the electrode plates with the glue joint being made as the wood is in motion. The speed of the wood will depend on its thickness.

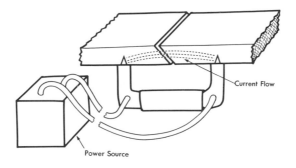

Fig. 13:3   Spot Gluing with Portable Dielectric Unit

is often referred to as *dielectric heating*.

Contact cement

This is a glue used to bond a plastic material, such as Arborite, to wood. Contact cement is a liquid, ready-prepared type of glue. As the name implies, the two surfaces to be joined together stick immediately on contact if they have both been coated with glue. A coat of the glue is spread on the two surfaces and allowed to dry for from 15 to 20 minutes or until it becomes tacky. They are then pressed together; no clamps are required.

Care must be taken when placing the two surfaces together to see that they are properly aligned, since it is almost impossible to move either of the parts once contact has been made.

Gluing stock together

When gluing stock together these points must be kept in mind:

1. Test the pieces for fit by clamping them together before gluing. This allows you to make adjustments in the fit, as well as to have the clamps adjusted and ready for use.

2. Have the glue and the room at the correct temperature.

3. When using bar clamps, place blocks between the clamps and the edge of the work.

4. Have all the necessary material such as glue, clamps, nails, hammer, screws, etc., available before starting to glue.

5. The surfaces to be glued must be free from dirt, grease, or other foreign matter.

6. Spread the glue with a brush or thin stick. If the glue is in a plastic squeeze bottle, it may be spread directly from the container. In industry a mechanical belt spreader is often used.

7. It is advisable in most cases to spread glue on both sides of the joint.

8. Use a sufficient number of clamps. If the joint is a long one, alternate them, using a moderate pressure. (See Figure 13:10.)

9. When gluing a joint, check to see that it is tight, flat, and square.

10. With a scrap of wood or a damp cloth, remove the surplus glue before it has set hard but after it has set slightly, so that it will not smear.

Clamps

There are three types of clamps used in general woodwork. These are:

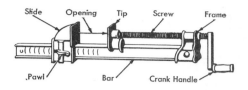

Fig. 13:4 Bar Clamp

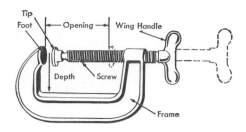

Fig. 13:6 C Clamp

(a) The *cabinet* or *bar clamp*, which is made in varying lengths from 2' to 6'. The length of each one can be adjusted by sliding the end section along the bar (see Figure 13:4).

(b) The *hand screw*, which consists of two hardwood jaws with two threaded screws with a handle on each. These clamps can be used with the jaws parallel or they can be tapered to fit an irregularly shaped piece of stock, as

shown in Figure 13:5. Hand screws are made in various sizes; use the size that suits the work to be glued.

(c) *The "C" clamp.* This is so named because of its shape and is an all-metal clamp. It is made in a large range of sizes from 2" to 16", the size being the distance the clamp will open when the screw is fully extended (see Figure 13:6).

The application of these clamps is shown in Figures 13:7 to 13:12.

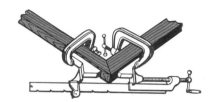

Fig. 13:7 Clamping Flat Mitre Joint with Use of Clamp Blocks

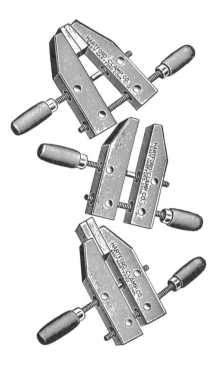

Hartford Clamp Co.

Fig. 13:5 Hand Screws, Sometimes Called Hand Clamps

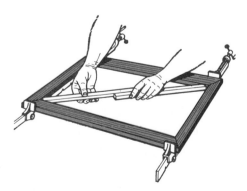

Fig. 13:8 Testing Squareness with Diagonals

78

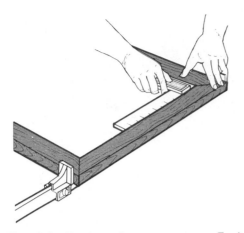

Fig. 13:9 Testing Squareness at Each Corner

When assembling a project that requires gluing and clamping, care must be taken to square up the project after the glue and the clamps have been applied and before the glue has set. If the work being assembled is square or rectangular, this can be done by measuring from opposite corners and adjusting the clamps to make the diagonal distances the same, as shown in Figure 13:8. In some cases it may be checked with a framing square (see Figure 13:9). Figure 13:11 illustrates an assembled project in clamps.

Holding tools

Clamps and hand screws are often used as holding tools, or as temporary vises, or to hold stop blocks to benches or machines. It is frequently necessary to clamp parts of a project together while they are being permanently fastened with nails or screws. Clamps are also used extensively in the bending of wood to shape, by clamping it to a form of the required shape. Three uses of hand screws as holding tools are shown in Figure 13:12.

Fig. 13:10

Fig. 13:11

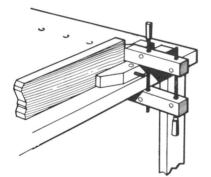

Stock Being Held for Edge Planing.

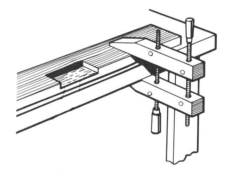

Holding Work Flat on the Bench.

For Holding Small Pieces.

Fig. 13:12

ASSIGNMENT

1. What evidence have we that glue has been in use for many centuries?
2. In what two forms are animal glues made?
3. (a) From what material is casein glue made? (b) What precautions must be taken when using casein glue?
4. State the advantages of prepared liquid resin glue.
5. Describe one method of creating the necessary heat when thermosetting glue is used for laminating wood.
6. List two types of glues that are water resistant and two that are not.
7. Which type of glue is used to laminate plastic materials to wood? How does it differ from other types of glue?
8. Explain the steps you would take, as well as the precautions you would observe, when making a large glue joint.
9. List three types of clamps, and give the special use of each.
10. How is an assembled project checked for squareness when it is being glued?
11. List two uses for a clamp as a holding tool other than the three shown in Figure 13:12.

CHAPTER FOURTEEN

band saws and jig saws

Band saws

There have been many improvements in the design and operation of band saws since the first one was made and patented by William Newbery in 1808 in England. Several types of band saws are made, each designed for a different kind of work. The largest is the *band mill*, which is used in sawmills for cutting logs into planks. This saw has wheels up to 7' in diameter and blades up to 16" wide. The *band resaw* is somewhat smaller and is used in mills and lumber yards for resawing thick lumber into thinner material. The type of saw used in small industrial shops, schools, and home workshops is the *band scroll saw*. This is a smaller general-purpose saw used for cutting curved and straight work, and is simply referred to as a *band saw*. This is the type shown in Figure 14:1 and described here.

All band saws operate in the same manner. The blade is a flexible strip of steel with teeth on the forward edge. The blade revolves round the two wheels as a belt round two pulleys. One of the wheels is power driven while the other is turned by the belt action of the blade. The parts of the band saw are shown in Figure 14:1. You should make yourself familiar with them.

The size of a band saw is determined by the diameter of the wheels. The 14", 20", and 30" are popular sizes for general work.

A rubber band or tire is fitted on the rim of the wheels. The top wheel can be adjusted up or down for the correct blade tension. It can also be tilted sideways for centring the blade on the rim so that it will track properly.

To prevent the blade from twisting, the band saw is equipped with an adjustable saw guide above the table, which also serves as a safety device. This guide has two hardened metal blocks, one on either side of the blade, to keep it in line. The guide is vertically adjustable and should be kept not more than ½" above the surface of the work. This serves to steady the blade and may prevent serious accidents. If the operator's fingers should slip off the work into the path of the blade they would be stopped by the guide. A guide is also placed below the table, which can be adjusted but not raised or lowered. Both guides have idler wheels or ball-bearing blade supports, which prevent the blade from being pushed off the back of the wheels. The blade support wheel should either be stopped or be turned slowly during normal operation of the saw. A saw guide is shown in Figure 14:2.

Most band saws may be equipped with cross-cut fences for making straight cuts either with or against the grain of the wood. A rip saw fence is shown in Figure 14:3.

How to use a band saw

The band saw is not a difficult machine to operate; in fact, the beginner can do a fairly good job on his first or second attempt at using it. However, there are some techniques that will help you to do a still better job.

Stand behind the blade and a little to the left. Feed the work with the right hand, which is held at the end of or far back on the work. The left hand is usually used to guide the work and is held at the edge of the work opposite

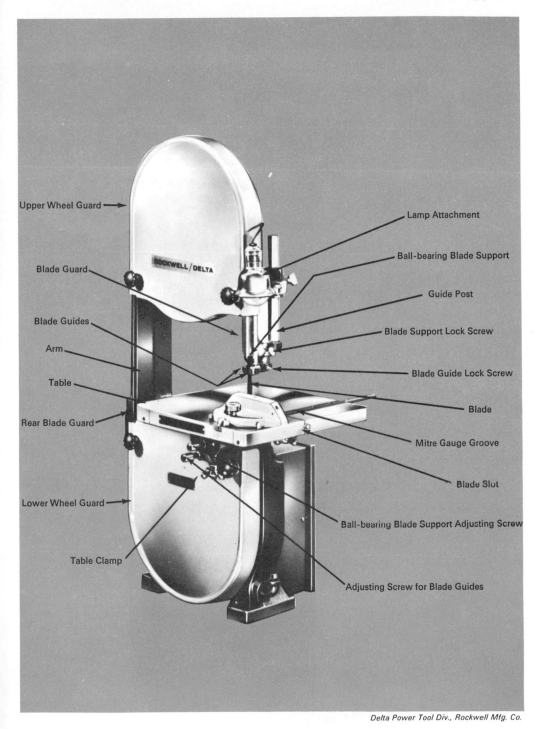

Upper Wheel Guard →

Lamp Attachment

Ball-bearing Blade Support

Blade Guard

ROCKWELL/DELTA

Guide Post

Blade Support Lock Screw

Blade Guides

Arm

Blade Guide Lock Screw

Table

Blade

Rear Blade Guard

Mitre Gauge Groove

Blade Slot

Lower Wheel Guard →

Ball-bearing Blade Support Adjusting Screw

Table Clamp

Adjusting Screw for Blade Guides

Delta Power Tool Div., Rockwell Mfg. Co.

Fig. 14:1   14″ Band Saw

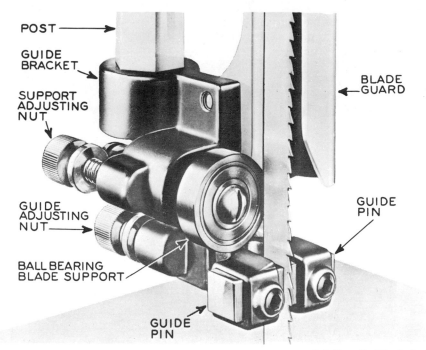

POST

GUIDE BRACKET

SUPPORT ADJUSTING NUT

GUIDE ADJUSTING NUT

BALL BEARING BLADE SUPPORT

GUIDE PIN

BLADE GUARD

GUIDE PIN

Delta Power Tool Div., Rockwell Mfg. Co.

Fig. 14:2 Band Saw Guide

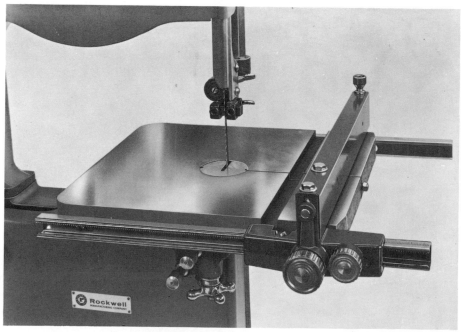

Rockwell Manufacturing Company

Fig. 14:3 Band Saw Fence

the blade. The position of the hands will necessarily depend to some extent on the size and shape of the piece to be cut.

Always outline the shape you wish to cut so that you have a guide line to follow. Cut on the waste side of this line, leaving the line on the work.

Do not crowd the saw or push the work into the blade too rapidly. Some experimenting will show you the correct speed for smooth and easy cutting.

Guide the work evenly around the curved cuts. As the blade cannot turn, the work must be moved. The size of arc that can be cut is determined by the width of the blade; the narrower the blade the smaller the radius that may be cut. A table indicating the minimum radius that may be cut with the various blade widths is shown below.

Blade Width	Minimum Radius
⅛″	¼″
³⁄₁₆″	½″
¼″	¾″
⅜″	1″
½″	1¼″
¾″	1¾″

Although the band saw is used mainly for cutting curves or irregular shapes, it can also be used for cross-cutting, ripping, or resawing. To resaw is to set the stock on edge and to saw the full width of the piece, thus making two or more pieces of equal thickness. For these operations a wider blade should be used if a considerable amount of material is to be cut.

Before you begin to make the saw cut, study the design and decide where to start and which cut to make first. Long curves or combination cuts such as are shown in Figure 14:4 should be broken up by making short, straight cuts. The saw blade can be backed out

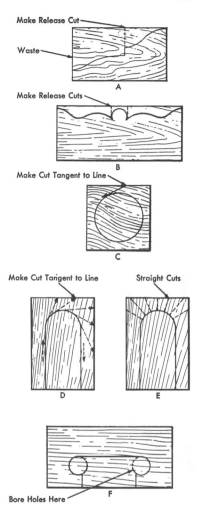

Fig. 14:4 Cutting Curved Shapes on the Band Saw

of these quite easily. This will prevent the blade from being trapped in an internal corner, from which the blade must be backtracked out of a long and difficult curve, a manoeuvre likely to pull the blade off the wheel. Figure 14:4 shows examples of various designs that might be cut; the arrows indicate the cuts to be made first.

A little thought before you start will save time later in finishing your work and prevent you from getting into difficulties.

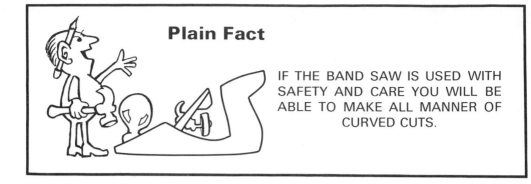

Plain Fact

IF THE BAND SAW IS USED WITH SAFETY AND CARE YOU WILL BE ABLE TO MAKE ALL MANNER OF CURVED CUTS.

Although the band saw is a comparatively safe machine to operate, there are some safety precautions that *must* be observed:

1. Place the upper saw guide *not* more than ½" above the work.

2. Pay close attention to the operation of the machine. Do not be distracted by anything or anyone. The saw requires your undivided attention.

3. See that the wheel guards are in place.

4. Do not start to cut until the saw has reached full speed.

5. Keep your fingers as far away from the blade as the size of the work will permit.

6. Use a push stick to move scrap pieces of wood away from the blade.

7. Keep the floor area around the saw clean.

8. Do not hesitate to seek assistance if you are not certain how to proceed or if you get into difficulty.

9. Do not use a wide blade if you are cutting small arcs.

10. Never leave the saw running and unattended.

11. If the blade breaks, shut off the power and stand clear until the wheels have stopped turning.

The scroll saw

This machine is more often referred to as a *jig saw*, but its correct name is the *scroll saw*. The scroll saw is used mainly for cutting fine, intricate shapes from thin stock. It is equally useful for cutting external or internal shapes (cutting out the centre portion of a pattern). The blades used are narrow, a factor which makes it possible to cut very sharp angles for fine work.

There is a considerable overlap in the jobs that can be performed on the band saw and the scroll saw. Many cutting operations can be done equally well on either machine. However, the band saw is restricted to cutting radii ¼" or more. Even for the ¼" radius a narrower blade is required than is used for general band saw work. The jig saw, on the other hand, is restricted as to the thickness of the work that can be cut. One inch should be the maximum thickness. It operates more efficiently with thin stock.

The principal mechanical part of the scroll saw is the cam shaft, a mechanical device that converts the circular motion of the belt-driven pully to the up-and-down motion required for the saw blade.

The size of a scroll saw is determined by the width of the throat, or the distance between the blade and the frame. The 24" size is the most popular.

The principal parts of a scroll saw are shown in Figure 14:5.

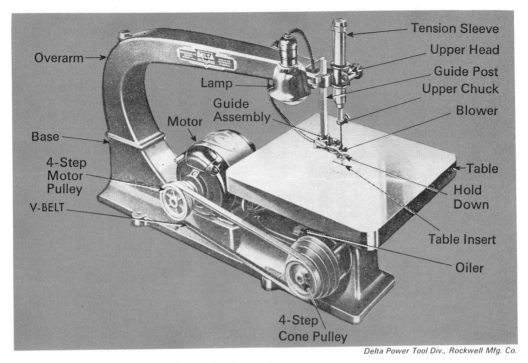

Overarm
Lamp
Guide Assembly
Motor
Base
4-Step Motor Pulley
V-BELT

Tension Sleeve
Upper Head
Guide Post
Upper Chuck
Blower
Table
Hold Down
Table Insert
Oiler

4-Step Cone Pulley

Delta Power Tool Div., Rockwell Mfg. Co.

Fig. 14:5 Scroll Saw or Jig Saw

The table on most scroll saws can be tilted for bevel cutting. There are two types of blades that may be used. The first is the jeweller's blade, which is fine and must be held in place by two chucks, one attached to the lower plunger, and one above the table attached to the upper plunger. This blade is used for fine work. The sabre blade is heavier and is attached only to the lower chuck with the top of the blade left free. This blade is fast-cutting and is used for heavier material when the curves are not too small. Figure 14:6 shows a jeweller's blade in place, and Figure 14:7 a sabre saw blade. A sanding attachment can be attached to the lower chuck, as shown in Figure 14:8.

The scroll saw is probably the simplest woodworking power tool to operate. However, there are a few rules that should be followed:

Delta Power Tool Div., Rockwell Mfg. Co.

Fig. 14:6 Jig Saw with Jeweller's Blade

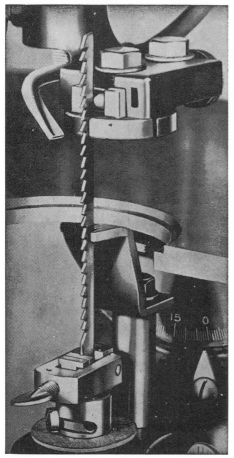

Fig. 14:7   Sabre Saw Blade

Fig. 14:8   (Left) Sanding Attachment on a Scroll Saw (Right) File Attachment on a Scroll Saw

The spring hold-down should rest on the work, pressing it firmly on the table to prevent the work from bobbing up and down with the action of the blade.

When the blade must be threaded through a hole to make an inside cut, you should release the blade from the upper chuck, and raise the tension sleeve and guide post. This will provide enough space for the work to go over the blade. If a sabre blade is used, it is necessary only to raise the guide post and the hold-down assembly.

Always have the points of the teeth pointing down so that the blade cuts on the down stroke.

Before starting to saw, it is important that you have a clear pencilled outline to follow. The outline may be transferred from a pattern by carbon paper or it may be drawn or laid out directly on the wood.

ASSIGNMENT

Band saw

1. Explain the operating principle of a band saw.
2. Why is a rubber tire used on the rim of the wheel?
3. How is a band saw blade tracked?
4. Describe the two purposes served by the band saw guide.
5. What is the purpose of a small idler wheel on the saw guide?
6. What is the smallest diameter circle than can be cut with a 3/16" blade? 1/4" blade? 3/8" blade?
7. Redraw the sketch shown here and indicate by numbered lines the or-

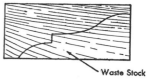

Waste Stock

der in which you would cut out this pattern.

8. List five safety precautions that must be observed while operating the band saw.

Jig saw

9. What is the main difference in the cutting action of the band saw and the scroll saw?

10. How is the size of a scroll saw determined? What is the most popular size?

11. What are the two types of blades used on scroll saws? How do they differ?

12. List the steps involved in setting up the jig saw for cutting an interior section of a pattern.

drill press and mortiser

Drill press

The drill press is a useful, versatile, and easily operated machine. It is often considered a machinist's tool because of its use for drilling holes in metals; however, it is also very adaptable to woodworking for such operations as boring, mortising, routing, and sanding, which can be performed with the aid of attachments.

The drill press (see Figure 15:1) consists of a vertical column set on a base. On the upper end of the column the motor and the drill spindle are mounted. The spindle is driven by a belt and cone pulley arrangement that can be moved up and down by operating a hand lever, or by a foot feed. The table can also be moved up or down on the column to accommodate work of different sizes. The table can be tilted to 45° for angle boring. A depth gauge is generally provided to control the depth of the holes.

Most drill presses are fitted with two cone pulleys, one on the motor and the other on the spindle, so that selective speeds can be obtained for various operations. The cone pulleys used vary in diameter, but the average speeds required for woodworking operations are 680, 1250, 2400, and 4600 revolutions per minute (rpm). The speeds are changed by moving the V belt from one step on the cone pulley to the other. Some drill presses are equipped with a third cone pulley for a greater variation of speeds (see Figure 15:2).

Drill presses are made in both floor and bench models, the only difference being the length of the column. A bench-type drill press is shown in Figure 15:1.

The bits used for boring holes with a drill press differ from those used in the hand brace. Since three-jawed chucks are used on the drill press, the bits must have a round shank in place of the square one used with the brace. Bits with a screw feed should not be used unless the speed of the drill press can be reduced to that of the lead of the screw; otherwise the bit will lift the work and it will spin with the bit. For this reason most bits used have brad points (ones with no threads). Large-size bits are sometimes referred to as *cutters*, which bore holes up to 3″ in diameter. Some of the bits used in a drill press are shown in Figures 15:3 to 15:7.

The speed at which the drill press should be operated for drilling in wood will depend on the diameter of the bit being used. For holes up to ¾″ in diameter the second lowest speed (about 1250 rpm) should be used. For larger bits and cutters the speed should be reduced to the slowest speed (about 680 rpm).

Drill press attachments

One of the most useful attachments that can be used with a drill press is the mortising attachment.

Mortising is the operation of making square or rectangular-shaped holes to receive the tenon half of a mortise-and-tenon joint. The square holes are made by placing a bit inside a hollow chisel. The bit revolves, removing the wood, and the square chisel slices the wood from the side of the hole as it is forced down by the drill press. This leaves a neat, square hole of the required size and depth.

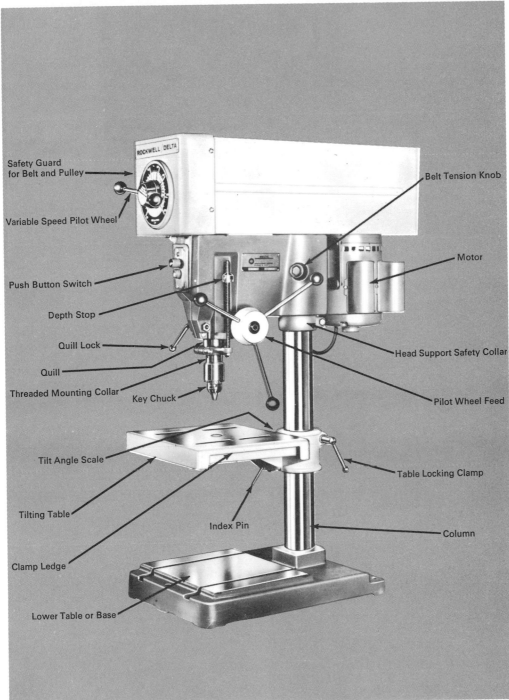

Safety Guard
for Belt and Pulley

Belt Tension Knob

Variable Speed Pilot Wheel

Motor

Push Button Switch

Depth Stop

Quill Lock

Head Support Safety Collar

Quill

Threaded Mounting Collar

Key Chuck

Pilot Wheel Feed

Tilt Angle Scale

Table Locking Clamp

Tilting Table

Index Pin

Column

Clamp Ledge

Lower Table or Base

Delta Power Tool Div., Rockwell Mfg. Co.

Fig. 15:1   15″ Drill Press

Delta Power Tool Div., Rockwell Mfg. Co.

Fig. 15:2   Cone Pulleys on a Drill Press

Fig. 15:3   Double Spur Drill Press Bit

Fig. 15:4   Multi-spur Bit

Fig. 15:5   Double Spur Drill Type

Stanley Tools

Stanley Tools

Fig. 15:6   Two Types of Power Centre Bits

Fig. 15:7   Adjustable Countersink Bit

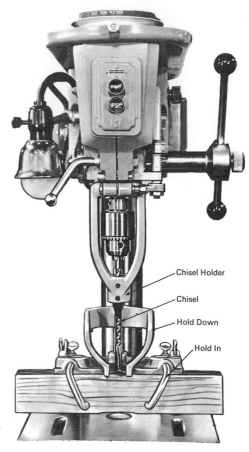

Chisel Holder

Chisel

Hold Down

Hold In

Delta Power Tool Div., Rockwell Mfg. Co.

Fig. 15:8   Mortising Attachment

Delta Power Tool Div., Rockwell Mfg. Co.

Fig. 15:9   Cutting a Design with a Router Bit

The mortising attachment is shown in Figure 15:8. Note the fence and hold-down and hold-in arrangements, which secure the work in place while the mortising is done. Since both the drill press and the mortiser require the same set-up for the mortising operation, the set-up procedure is described with the mortiser on pages 96-7.

Another important operation that can be performed with the drill press is *routing*, cutting a continuous hole or groove. This type of cut is used for inlay work and many other special purposes. Figure 15:9 illustrates one application of a router bit: cutting an inlay design.

Special bits or cutters are used for routing. A short, fluted, flat-bottomed bit is generally used (see Figure 15:11). The bit may be fastened in the chuck or in some cases a special collar is used on the spindle of the drill press to hold the router bit more firmly.

Several rules should be followed when using a router bit with a drill press:

(a) The work must be fed into the bit against the rotation of the bit.

(b) For making straight cuts a fence must be used to guide the work. Slide the work along the fence so that the rotation of the bit will force the work against the fence. This generally means that the work should be moved from left to right, as shown in Figure 15:12.

(c) Only light ⅛" cuts should be made. If deeper cuts are required, several passes should be made. When heavy cuts are made, the cutter tends to grab the work and tear pieces of wood out instead of making a smooth cut.

(d) The drill should be running at high speeds to make a smooth cut with a router bit.

(e) Keep the bits sharp. For curved cuts, special set-ups involving some type

Fig. 15:10 Fluted Router Bit

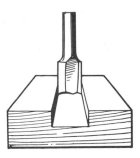

Fig. 15:11 Router Bit with Small Shank

of guide arrangements should be used. One of these is shown in Figure 15:17.

Shaping can be done on the drill press by using special cutter knives. Mouldings can be cut on the edge of stock by using any one of a great number of cutters available, or a combination of several cutters may be used to cut almost any desired design on the edge of the work. Some of the possible shapes are shown in Figure 15:13. More is said about shaping in Chapter 18.

Fig. 15:12 Note the direction of the feed.

93

These Shapes Cut with the Hole Cutters Shown in Fig. 15:15

Shapes Cut with One-piece Cutter

Fig. 15:13

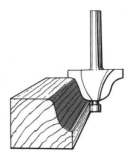

Fig. 15:14 Straight Cutter

There are two types of cutters in general use:

(a) The straight cutter, which can be used in the drill chuck, such as the one shown in Figure 15:14.

(b) The hole cutter, which is made with three cutting surfaces with a hole in the centre. This cutter fits over a spindle with a collar attached. The collar rides on the edge of the work and governs the depth of the cut to be made. Some of these cutters are shown in Figure 15:15. For straight work a fence should be used; for curved edges a collar or the round part of the cutter acts as the guide.

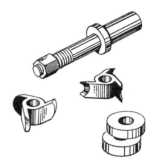

Fig. 15:15 Hole Cutters

As for routing, the cutter must travel at a high speed for shaping: 4600 rpm makes a smooth shaping operation. To prevent burning, keep the bits sharp and the work moving past the cutter. If the work is allowed to remain stationary while in contact with the revolving cutter, the moulded edge will be burned or discoloured.

Shaping can also be done with the router or spindle shaper if they are available. These machines are described in Chapter 18.

Some sanding operations can be performed on the drill press to advantage,

Plain Fact

THE DRILL PRESS IS A MOST USEFUL MACHINE; IT CAN SERVE NOT ONLY FOR DRILLING, BUT ALSO FOR MORTISING, ROUTING, SHAPING, AND SANDING. WHEN PROPERLY SET UP IT IS EASY TO OPERATE AND SAFE TO USE.

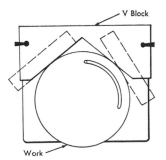

Fig. 15:16 Inlay Work on Curved Edges

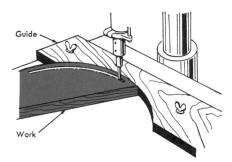

Fig. 15:17 Inlay Work on Curved Edges

Delta Power Tool Div., Rockwell Mfg. Co.

Fig. 15:18 Drum Sanders

especially on curved surfaces. Sanding drums of various sizes are used. They generally consist of a metal shaft, a rubber drum, and a garnet sandpaper sleeve. The sandpaper is slid over the rubber drum and the nut on the end tightened. This expands the rubber, making the paper tight. Sandpaper sleeves in various grits and diameters are available for this operation. Three sizes are shown in Figure 15:18.

Safety precautions for the drill press

(a) When boring small pieces, hold them securely with a clamp.

(b) Be sure to use a bottoming piece under the work so that you will not drill into the table.

(c) Operate the drill only at the correct speed.

(d) Make sure the bit is tight in the chuck.

(e) Locate the centre of the hole with an awl. Do not work by guess.

(f) Always switch off the drill before leaving it.

Hollow chisel mortiser

The mortiser is a machine designed exclusively for mortising. It performs the same operation as the mortising attachment for the drill press. The same types of bits and chisels are used in both machines. However, these operations can be performed faster and more efficiently on the mortiser because it is a heavier, more powerful machine designed especially for this operation.

There are two general types of mortisers: (a) the *hollow chisel mortiser*, and (b) the *chain saw mortiser*, where the wood is removed from the mortise by an endless chain saw arrangement

95

that rotates around two sprockets. The hollow chisel type is the most common and is the one that we will describe here. It can be used for most general types of mortising and is easily set up and operated. One type of modern hollow chisel mortiser is shown in Figure 15:19. Another type of hollow chisel mortiser that is in wide use has a foot feed. The table on this machine generally moves up and down, with the motor unit held stationary on the frame. Both machines use a similar type of clamping arrangement, as shown on the mortiser in Figure 15:19.

Certain main parts make up the hollow chisel mortiser shown here. The motor head can be moved up or down by means of a lever. The motor unit slides on dovetailed ways, which keeps it in a perfectly vertical position. The table may be moved in a horizontal plane either to the right or to the left, in toward the main column, or out toward the operator, which enables him to cut a fairly long mortise without resetting the stock in the clamps on the table. There is a fence at the back of the table, and an adjustable clamp that holds the work fimly against this fence at the correct location while the cut is being made. The upper end of the hollow chisel fits into a bushing, which, in turn, is attached to the motor shaft. The bit, which fits inside the chisel, revolves and removes the bulk of the wood, leaving only a small amount of wood in the corners to be cut out by the chisel.

The machine can be set to cut any desired depth of mortise. Care must be taken to allow clearance between the bit and the chisel or the bit will heat up in operation.

To set up and cut the mortise

The set-up of the mortiser for cutting any particular mortise will depend to some extent on the make of the machine. Care must be taken to attach the

Wadkin

Fig. 15:19 Hollow Chisel Mortiser

Wadkin

Fig. 15:20 Hollow Chisel and Bit

chisel properly in the bushing and sleeve, and to secure the work on the table in the correct location.

The general steps that are listed here should be adaptable to most makes of hollow chisel mortisers as well as to the mortising attachment for the drill press.

1. Lay out the position of the mortise on the stock. If several pieces with

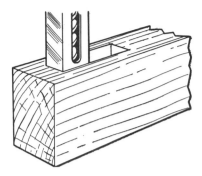

Fig. 15:21 Mortise Bit in the Work

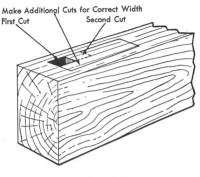

Fig. 15:23

identical mortises are to be cut, the layout need be made on only one piece.

2. Lower the chisel to the face of the work and adjust the fence so that the edge of the chisel will cut on the edge of the layout, as shown in Figure 15:21.

3. Mark the correct depth of the cut on the end of the stock. Set the chisel to this depth, as illustrated in Figure 15:22. Set the depth gauge arrangement.

4. Tighten the clamps and the hold-down arrangement to secure the work firmly in position.

5. Make the first cut at the start of the mortise. Lift the chisel often to clear the chips and prevent it from overheating.

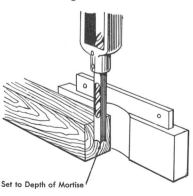

Set to Depth of Mortise

Fig. 15:22

6. Move the table or the work ahead three-quarters of the width of the mortise and make another cut.

7. Continue making cuts until the end of the mortise is reached. To make the mortise the exact length required, it is advisable to make the two end cuts first.

8. Wherever possible the hollow chisel used should be the same size as the width of the mortise. However, where a width of mortise other than a standard-sized chisel is required or where the correct size is not available, additional cuts must be made, as shown in Figure 15:23.

Bits and chisels commonly come in $\frac{1}{4}$", $\frac{5}{16}$", $\frac{3}{8}$", $\frac{1}{2}$", $\frac{5}{8}$", $\frac{3}{4}$", and 1" sizes. The spindle speed of most mortisers is from 3000 to 3600 rpm. If a mortise attachment is being used on the drill press, the belt should be on the second highest speed (2400 rpm).

ASSIGNMENT

Drill press

1. What operations can be performed on the drill press?

2. What are the four speeds generally used for the drill press?

3. If you wish to increase the speed of the drill press, would you (a) move the belt to a larger section of the cone pulley on the drill spindle, or (b) move the belt to a larger section of the cone pulley on the motor?

4. When a third cone pulley is used, as is shown in Figure 15:2, how many different speeds may be obtained?

5. How do bits used on a drill press differ from those used with a hand brace?

6. What is the recommended drill speed for a ½" bit?

7. List four types of bits that may be used on a drill press.

8. Explain how the mortise bit and chisel operate to cut a square hole.

9. List three safety rules that must be observed while operating the drill press.

10. For what purpose other than inlay work might you require the routing operation?

11. When routing, why should the work be fed into the bit against the rotation of the bit? Why should only light cuts be taken?

12. What is meant by shaping with a drill press? What types of bit or cutter are used?

13. At what speed should the bit be travelling for the routing or shaping operation?

14. If the motor speed is 1450 rpm, and the belt is running from the 4" step of its cone pulley to the 6" step on the cone pulley on the drill press, what would be the rpm of the drill chuck?

Mortising

15. List two types of mortisers.

16. What advantage does a hollow chisel mortising machine have over the mortising attachment on a drill press?

17. How is the work held in the correct position when making a mortise cut?

18. List the first four steps required in the mortising operation.

19. In what standard sizes are hollow chisels made for use on a mortiser?

20. With the aid of a sketch, explain the order of the cuts required to cut a mortise $9/16$" wide and 2½" long on the mortiser.

CHAPTER SIXTEEN

sanders

Stationary sanders

There are four types of stationary sanders used in wood shops. They are the disc sander, belt sander, spindle sander, and drum sander. Some machines are a combination of these.

Disc sanders

The disc sander is a good general-purpose sander that is to be found in most school shops. One of these sanders is shown in Figure 16:1. It is generally equipped with a mitre gauge which fits into a recess in the table. The gauge can be set at any desired angle for accurate sanding (see Figure 16:2). The table can be tilted to any angle up to 45°, so that by using the mitre gauge and the tilted table compound angles may be sanded.

The metal disc is attached to the shaft of the motor, making this sander a direct drive machine. The sandpaper disc must be mounted smoothly on the machined surface of the metal to make a true surface for accurate sanding. A special type of disc adhesive, which is available in a stick form, is applied to the metal disc as it rotates. Adhesive is also rubbed on the back of the sandpaper, which is then applied to the metal; the surfaces stick on contact. The old adhesive must be removed from the metal before the new coating

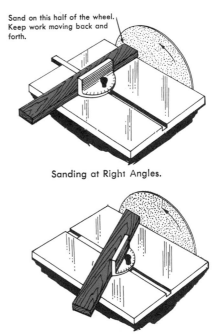

Sand on this half of the wheel. Keep work moving back and forth.

Sanding at Right Angles.

Angle Sanding. Some Sanders Rotate to the Right.

General Mfg. Co.

Fig. 16:1   Disc Sander

Fig. 16:2   Mitre Gauge Settings

Fig. 16:3 Sander Table Tilted

is applied. This procedure is illustrated in Figure 16:4.

The size of a disc sander is designated by the diameter of the disc, 12″ being the one most commonly used.

Belt sanders

Belt sanders are better for many operations than disc sanders because the sanding can be done in the direction of the grain instead of across it or in a circular motion. There are many sizes and types of belt sanders, but they all have the same principle of operation. An endless belt of sandpaper runs around two drums, one of which is power driven. Some of them are equipped with a table and a mitre gauge similar to those used on the disc sander. The smaller belt sanders will operate vertically, horizontally, or at any angle in between, as shown in Figures 16:6 and 16:7. A fence may be attached to the side of the belt for sanding an edge straight (see Figure 16:8). A combination sander, which incorporates both a disc and a belt, is also often used.

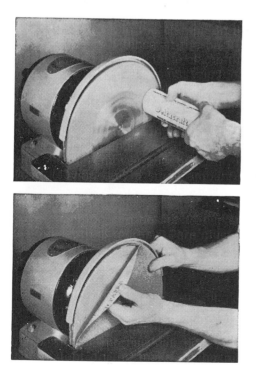

Fig. 16:4 Applying Sandpaper Disc to Sander

Fig. 16:7   Using Table and Mitre Gauge

Fig. 16:5   Belt Sander

Fig. 16:8   Sanding with a Fence

Fig. 16:6   In Horizontal Position

Belt stroke sanders

Figure 16:9 illustrates a belt stroke sander. This is an efficient type of sander that is in use in many school and industrial woodworking shops. The work is placed on the table, and the hand block is held on the smooth side of the paper, forcing the cutting side into contact with the work (see Figure 16:10). A light or a heavy cut can be

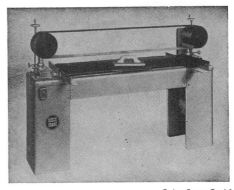

Fig. 16:9   Belt Stroke Sander

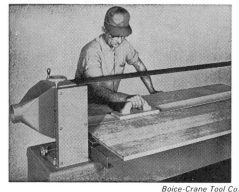

Boice-Crane Tool Co.

Fig. 16:10 Sanding Flat Stock Using a
Hand Block

made by varying the pressure on the
hand block. One drum is motor-driven
while the other, the idler drum, may be
moved to force the sandpaper belt
down onto the surface of the work.
These machines are quite versatile and
can be used in several ways, as shown
in Figures 16:11 and 16:12.

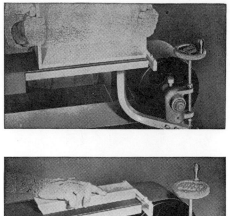

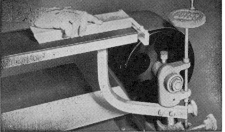

Boice-Crane Tool Co.

Fig. 16:12 Sanding Using Auxiliary Table

Feed belt sanders

Precision sanding is done on feed belt
sanders, which operate similarly to
planers, where the thickness of the
stock can be controlled. The main purpose of a feed sander is to finish
panels, doors, and flat trim stock.

Drum sanders

To obtain a perfectly flat, true surface
on wide surfaces such as doors or
panels that are more than 24" wide,
drum sanders are used. These sanders
are produced in various sizes up to 52"
in width. The diameters of the drums
may vary from 6" to 24". There are two
basic types of drum sanders, the single
drum and the multiple drum. Figure
16:14 illustrates the latter, with three
12" drums. The work is fed into the
machine by a revolving rubber belt over
the table. The thickness of the sanded
material can be strictly controlled on
this machine.

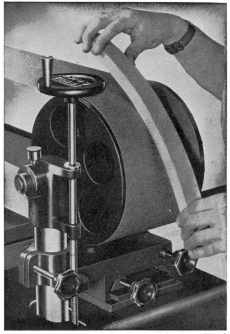

Boice-Crane Tool Co.

Fig. 16:11 Sanding Using the Drum

102

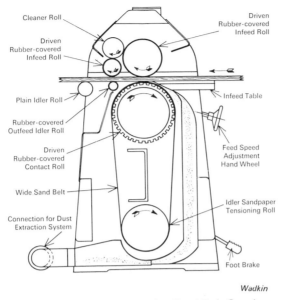

Cleaner Roll

Driven Rubber-covered Infeed Roll

Driven Rubber-covered Infeed Roll

Plain Idler Roll

Infeed Table

Rubber-covered Outfeed Idler Roll

Driven Rubber-covered Contact Roll

Feed Speed Adjustment Hand Wheel

Wide Sand Belt

Idler Sandpaper Tensioning Roll

Connection for Dust Extraction System

Foot Brake

Wadkin

Fig. 16:13 Operation of a Feed Belt Sander

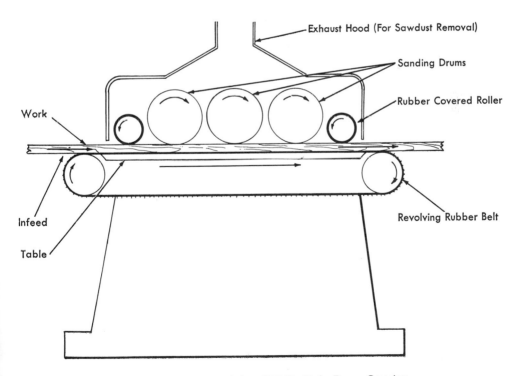

Exhaust Hood (For Sawdust Removal)

Sanding Drums

Rubber Covered Roller

Work

Revolving Rubber Belt

Infeed

Table

Fig. 16:14 Operation of the 48" Multiple Drum Sander

103

Fig. 16:15 Vertical Spindle Sander

Wadkin

Porter-Cable

Fig. 16:16 Orbital Sander

Orbital sanders

This type operates by moving the sanding pad in a ¼" circle or orbit. It does an efficient job on a flat surface and is especially good for close quarters or recessed panels. However, some hand sanding with fine paper, rubbing in the direction of the grain, is necessary to complete the sanding job. This will erase any very fine circular scratches left by a power sander. An orbital sander is shown in Figure 16:16.

Oscillating sanders

The oscillating sander is similar in shape and design to the orbital sander, but it operates differently in that the sandpaper pad moves back and forth in a straight line. It therefore makes a finer finish with no circular scratches. The sanding is done with the grain of the wood and for this reason it is often referred to as a finishing sander. Both of these sanders may be operated by electricity or compressed air.

Belt sanders

The belt sander (Figure 16:17) can also be used with the grain of the wood, and if sufficiently fine paper is used, very little hand sanding is required on flat surfaces. Care must be taken when operating the belt sander to keep it in motion in order to prevent it from digging into the wood. It should be moved

Spindle sanders

A spindle sander can be used to advantage when sanding inside curves or radii. The diameters of the spindles vary from ½" to 6" and the lengths from 6" to 9". On many machines the spindle moves up and down as well as rotating. This does a better sanding job and wears the sandpaper more evenly. Spindle sanders are sometimes referred to as *bobbin* or *oscillating sanders*. The sandpaper is made up in sleeves, which can be slid over the spindles. A vertical spindle sander is shown in Figure 16:15.

A spindle sanding arrangement is often incorporated into the disc sander, with the spindle in a horizontal position.

Portable sanders

There are three general types of portable sanders:

104

Plain Fact

A SANDER IS *NOT* A PLANER. IT SHOULD BE USED *ONLY* FOR LIGHT FINISHING, NOT FOR REMOVING LARGE QUANTITIES OF WOOD.

backwards and forwards the full length of the work and on each stroke should be moved sideways half the width of the belt. The belts are made up and sold in coarse, medium, and fine grades. Any of these three types of portable sanders may be equipped with a vacuum bag.

Safety precautions for the sander

1. Before starting, make sure the disc or belt is not torn or loose.

2. Do not start or stop the sander while it is resting on the work, on the bench, or on loose material.

3. Check the angle of the table before using the disc sander.

Stanley Power Tools

Fig. 16:17 Belt Sander

4. Make certain no loose clothing can be trapped between the moving belt and the housing of the machine.

5. Sand work *only* on the down side of the disc. Note the direction in which the disc is revolving before starting to sand.

6. Hold the work firmly on the table, *not* above the table or in any other unsupported position.

7. Use the correct grade of abrasive paper: coarse for general work and fine for finish cuts.

8. Keep your fingers away from the abrasive surface. Sandpaper is sharp and will cut anything.

9. Keep the work moving across the abrasive surface. Holding it in one place will burn and discolour the surface.

10. If the sander is equipped with a suction dust collector, turn it on before starting to sand.

11. Do not go away and leave the machine running.

ASSIGNMENT

1. List four types of stationary sanders and two types of portable sanders.

105

2. (a) What is meant by a compound angle on a piece of stock? (See Glossary of Terms.)
   (b) How is this type of angle sanded on the disc sander?

3. What is the procedure for mounting the sandpaper on the disc sander?

4. How does the cutting action of the belt sander differ from that of the disc sander?

5. Explain how flat work is sanded on the belt stroke sander.

6. Make a sketch showing the principle of operation of the feed belt sander.

7. How is the work drawn into a drum sander?

8. What type of work is generally sanded on (a) a drum sander? (b) a spindle sander?

9. Why is it an advantage, on a vertical spindle sander, to have the spindle move up and down as well as revolve?

10. List four safety rules that must be observed while operating the sander.

11. State one advantage of the portable belt sander over the orbital sander.

12. How should you operate a portable belt sander on a large flat section to ensure a true flat surface?

CHAPTER SEVENTEEN

wood lathe

The wood turning lathe enjoys a special place among all woodworking machines. It is probably the oldest of all furniture-making and craft machines, a crude hand-operated lathe having been invented about 1000 B.C. The lathe combines the art of hand tool work and the mechanical operation of a modern machine, and may be considered as a single manufacturing unit in itself on which a complete project may be made without the aid of other machines.

Most other woodworking machines have revolving knives or blades that pass over or through the work. The operation of the lathe is different: the work is revolved and the cutting tools are held firmly on a rest.

The lathe is not a difficult machine to operate, but the ability to produce good turnings quickly and accurately requires considerable skill. This can be acquired only by a knowledge of the correct methods of turning, and practice in the use of the lathe. The art of wood turning depends largely on the skilful manipulation of the chisels by hand.

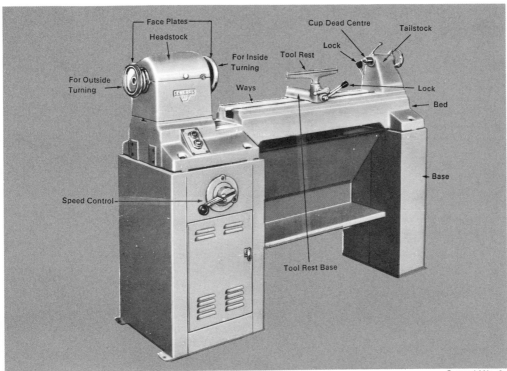

General Mfg. Co.

Fig. 17:1   Wood Lathe

Parts of a lathe

The wood lathe is often referred to as a *speed lathe*. This distinguishes it from a screw-cutting metal lathe. A typical wood lathe is shown in Figure 17:1. The principal parts are the bed, the headstock, the tailstock, and the tool rest. The *bed* is the main "I"-beam-shaped cast iron base; the upper surface is machined and is called the *ways*. The *headstock* is the business end of the lathe that makes the wood revolve. It consists of a hollow spindle on which the *pulley* is attached at one end and the *spur* or *live centre* at the other. The spur on most lathes is held to the hollow spindle by a friction fit, the spindle being internally ground to a No. 2 morse taper and the shank of the spur having an identical taper to fit into it. The spur can easily be removed by inserting a lathe rod through the hollow shaft from the pulley end and tapping the spur.

The *tailstock* is machined so that it slides along the ways and can be clamped at any desired spot. The *dead centre* is mounted in the tailstock in the same manner that the live centre is held in the headstock. The two centres are the same height from the bed and are in line with each other. There are two types of dead centre: (a) the *cup centre*, and (b) the *cone centre*. These are illustrated in Figure 17:2. The cup centre is the one used on most modern lathes because it does not require that a hole be drilled to centre the stock.

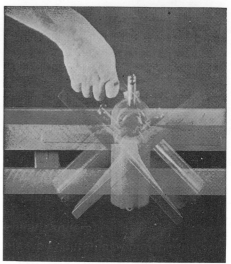

Delta Power Tool Div., Rockwell Mfg. Co.

Fig. 17:3   Movement of the Tool Rest

The *tool rest* is an important part of the lathe. It consists of two parts: the base, which can be slid along the bed, and the tool rest, which fits into the base and may be raised or lowered. Different-sized tool rests may be fitted into a standard tool rest base (see Figure 17:3).

Turning

There are two general types of wood turning:

1. *Spindle turning* — turning work between centres.

2. *Face plate turning* — mounting and turning the work on a flat metal face plate that is attached to the headstock in place of the spur centre.

Spindle turning

Most lathe work is done by spindle turning for such things as lamps and table legs. The first operation in this type of turning is to centre the ends of the stock. This is done by one of two simple methods. The first method is

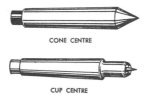

CONE CENTRE

CUP CENTRE

Fig. 17:2   Lathe Centres

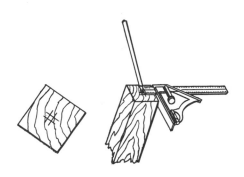

Fig. 17:4   Centring Stock

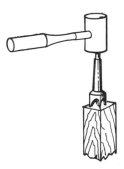

Fig. 17:6   Centring Stock

shown in Figure 17:4, where a distance a little less or a little more than one-half the width of the material is marked off; the centre of the small square thus formed can easily be found and used as the true centre of the work. The second and simpler method of locating the centre is to draw diagonal lines from corner to corner, the centre being at the intersection of the lines.

After the centre has been located on both ends of the work, use the scratch awl to definitely mark this centre. If hardwood is used, drill a small hole in one end, and make a saw cut about an ⅛" deep on the diagonal lines. The spur is then placed against the end and tapped with a mallet so that it is well seated, with the spur teeth firmly in the saw cuts.

Fig. 17:5   Centring Stock

To mount the work in the lathe

Hold the material against the spur and move the tailstock to within 1" of the end of the piece and lock it in position. Turn the tailstock spindle until it makes contact with the wood. Place a few drops of oil or grease on the centre and continue turning out the centre until it is snug; then loosen it off slightly. Before locking the tailstock spindle, check to see that the work turns freely but has no side play or looseness between the centres.

Set the tool rest so that it is slightly above the centre of the work (not more than ¼"). It should be set from ⅛" to ⅜" from the work and parallel with it.

Face plate turning

Work such as lamp bases and bowls, which cannot be turned between centres, is mounted on a face plate.

The face plates used vary in diameter according to the work to be turned, from the screw plate shown in Figure 17:7 to an 8" plate used for large work on outside turning. The work may be mounted directly on the face plate with short but heavy wood screws, or a backing block may be used (see Figure 17:8). When a backing block is used, it may be screwed to the work, or it may be glued with a piece of paper between it and the work. When the finished work is separated from the backing

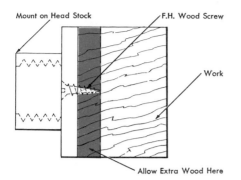

Mount on Head Stock — F.H. Wood Screw

Work

Allow Extra Wood Here

Fig. 17:7 Screw Plate

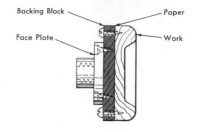

Backing Block — Paper

Face Plate — Work

Fig. 17:8 Use of a Backing Block

Fig. 17:9 Work Mounted Directly on Face Plate

block, the paper will split, leaving the finished turning undamaged.

The terms *inside turning* and *outside turning* refer to the location of the face plate on the lathe, as shown in Figure 17:1. For an inside face plate turning, the spur is removed and the face plate screwed to the spindle at this point, as shown in Figure 17:10. The size of the work that can be turned here is determined by the distance from the bed to the lathe centre. This is called the *swing* of the lathe, which designates the size of the machine. On most general-purpose lathes this distance is 6", so that 12" is the maximum diameter for inside turning. For outside turning, work of a larger diameter is turned on the outboard end of the headstock, as shown in Figure 17:11. A floor stand rest must be used for this outside turning.

Methods of wood turning

There are two generally accepted methods of wood turning: (a) the *cutting method* and (b) the *scraping* or *pattern maker's method*. The cutting method is the one used most often as it is faster and easier on the cutting tools, although it requires more skill. The scraping method is a slower but more accurate method. Both have their advantages and each should be used for

Delta Power Tool Div., Rockwell Mfg. Co.

Fig. 17:10 Roughing the Work to Size with a Gouge

Delta Power Tool Div., Rockwell Mfg. Co.

Fig. 17:11 Making the Finishing Cut with a Spear-point chisel

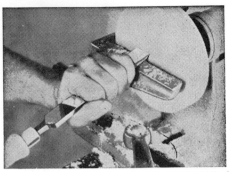

Delta Power Tool Div., Rockwell Mfg. Co.

Fig. 17:12 Facing the Work with a Square-nosed or Skew Chisel

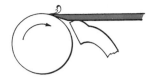

Fig. 17:14 Cutting Method of Turning

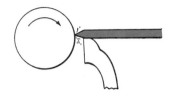

Fig. 17:15 Scraping Method of Turning

Delta Power Tool Div., Rockwell Mfg. Co.

Fig. 17:13 Shaping the Face with a Round-nosed Chisel. Note the position of the hands and the firm grip on the chisel.

specific operations. When using the cutting method, the chisel should be held at an angle, with the handle lower than the cutting edge. This makes the cutting edge tangential to the circle or surface of the cylinder to be cut, so that the wood is sliced or peeled off. The scraping tool should be held in a horizontal position and flat on the tool rest to make a fine, smooth, scraping cut (see Figures 17:14 and 17:15).

Wood turning tools

The standard set of wood turning tools consists of the five shapes illustrated in Figure 17:16. Although there are several sizes of each type, practically all turning can be done with these five basic chisels. The *gouge* is used for roughing the square stock down to about ⅛" larger than the diameter required. It can also be used for cutting grooves or for any heavy cutting. When starting to remove the rough stock with a gouge, take small cuts, working from the centre towards the end of the stock to prevent splintering the wood at the ends. The cutting edge of the gouge must be ahead of the handle as it is pushed across the work. The gouge should be held as shown in Figure 17:17.

The *skew* is probably the most useful and versatile of all wood turning tools. It can be used for many operations. One of these is to bring a cylinder to exact size after it has been rough-turned with the gouge. This should be done with a shearing cut by holding the chisel at an angle, as shown in Figure 17:19. Start the cut an inch or two in from the end, and work towards either end. To be able to make a good shear cut with the skew tipped at this angle takes considerable skill gained from practice and effort. The cutting of shoulders, V's, and beads, and the squaring of an end are some of the other uses of the skew chisel.

111

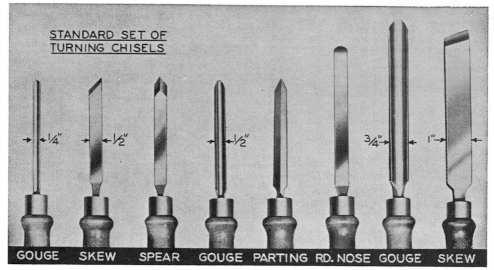

STANDARD SET OF TURNING CHISELS

GOUGE   SKEW   SPEAR   GOUGE   PARTING   RD. NOSE   GOUGE   SKEW

Delta Power Tool Div., Rockwell Mfg. Co.

Fig. 17:16 Standard Set of Turning Chisels

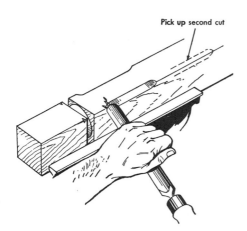

Pick up second cut

Fig. 17:17 Rough Turning with Gouge

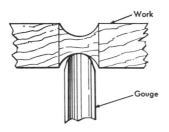

Work

Gouge

Fig. 17:18

Delta Power Tool Div., Rockwell Mfg. Co.

Fig. 17:19 Bringing Work to Size with a Skew

Fig. 17:20 Angle of Skew for Shearing Cut

Delta Power Tool Div., Rockwell Mfg. Co.

Fig. 17:21 Care must be taken not to allow the toe or point of the skew to be caught in the revolving work.

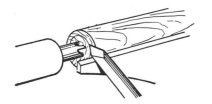
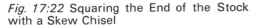

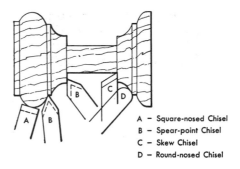

A - Square-nosed Chisel
B - Spear-point Chisel
C - Skew Chisel
D - Round-nosed Chisel

Fig. 17:24 Uses of Chisels

Fig. 17:22 Squaring the End of the Stock with a Skew Chisel

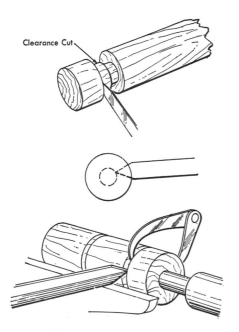

Fig. 17:23 Parting Chisel Used to Make Sizing Cuts

The *parting tool* is a lathe tool easy to use. It cuts with a scraping action and needs only to be pushed into the wood. For better cutting, lower the handle so that the cutting edge is slightly above centre. This tool is used mainly for depth cuts and is used in conjunction with calipers. When making a deep cut with the parting tool, a clearance cut must be made beside the first cut to prevent over-heating of the point.

Figure 17:24 shows the *round-nosed* and *spear turning chisels* being used to advantage. These tools are used more in face plate turning than in spindle turning because the scraping operation is safer and easier when cutting end grain.

Pointers on spindle turning

1. After mounting work in the lathe, rough-turn it to the largest diameter with the large gouge.

2. Make a smoothing cut with the skew and check the diameter with outside calipers.

3. Mark off the positions of the required dimensions. If the pencil marks are made about ½″ long, they can be seen while the work is rotating. Lines all the way round the piece can be made with the pencil point while the work revolves.

4. With the parting tool, cut the work to the correct diameter at the marks, as shown in Figure 17:23 (b).

5. With the appropriate tool, cut away the wood between the parting tool cuts.

6. Remove the tool rest and sand the work. When several turnings of the same pattern are required, cardboard or metal patterns are often made so that exact duplicate turnings can be made (see Figure 17:25).

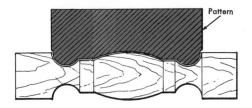

Fig. 17:25 Work Turned to Fit Pattern

Safety precautions for the lathe

The lathe is a comparatively safe machine to operate. However, there are precautions that must be observed when using it.

1. One of the most important safety devices on the modern lathe is the variable speed arrangement, which consists of a cone pulley on the lathe and a corresponding cone pulley on the motor. The more modern lathes are equipped with a variable speed V pulley arrangement whereby the lathe speed can be changed by means of turning a lever, without the necessity of changing the belt. Many accidents have occurred because the work was revolving too fast. The speed of the lathe should be determined by the diameter of the work being turned; the smaller the diameter of the work, the greater the rpm

should be. The following table will serve as a guide for turning speeds.

Diameter for Spindle Turning	Diameter for Face Plate Turning	Recommended rpm
7" and over	11" and over	750
4" — 7"	9" — 11"	1100
2" — 4"	6" — 9"	1600
2" and under	6" and under	2600

2. Keep the tool rest close to the work, never more than ⅜" from the largest diameter.

3. Hold the turning chisel firmly, with one hand near the end of the handle and the other hand near the tool rest, as shown in Figure 17:10.

4. Remove the tool rest before sanding the work.

5. Safety goggles must be worn while operating the lathe.

6. Do not wear loose clothing that might get caught in the revolving work.

7. Do not make adjustments on the machine while it is in operation.

8. Keep the turning tools sharp.

Plain Fact

WOOD TURNING IS AN ART FORM THAT IS DEVELOPED BY ONE'S IMAGINATION IN DEVISING PLEASING SHAPES AND ONE'S SKILL IN THE USE OF TURNING TOOLS.

ASSIGNMENT

1. How does the lathe differ in principle from other woodworking machines?
2. What are the four main parts of a wood lathe?
3. What are the two general types of wood turning? How do they differ?
4. With the aid of a sketch explain two methods of centring stock for the lathe.
5. List the steps in setting up the stock in the lathe for spindle turning.
6. Where should the tool rest be set in relation to the work?
7. What is the purpose of using a backing block for face plate turning?
8. Explain what is meant by inside and outside face plate turning.
9. List the advantages and disadvantages of the scraping and the cutting methods of wood turning.
10. List the five basic chisels used in wood turning.

11. List the chisels in the order in which you would use them in turning this design on a piece of stock. Indicate where you would use each.

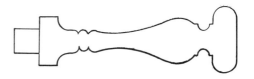

12. Why are scraping tools generally used for face plate turning?
13. If you wish to turn twenty baseball bats to exact regulation size, what method would you use to ensure a uniform size?
14. What should the rpm of the lathe be if you were spindle turning a piece of stock (a) 3" in diameter? (b) 8" in diameter? If you were face plate turning a piece of stock (a) 5" in diameter? (b) 10" in diameter?

CHAPTER EIGHTEEN

shaping and routing

Shaping refers to an operation in which wood is cut by knives or cutters that rotate horizontally, with the shaft in a vertical position. This is the opposite to the cutting action of a circular saw blade, where the blade is in a vertical position and the shaft is horizontal. These two methods of cutting are illustrated in Figure 18:1.

The shaping operation cuts irregular shapes to a definite design and produces a finished edge in one operation. A good example of this is the moulded edge on a straight or curved table top.

Routing is the cutting of a recess or a groove that does not go all the way through the stock, and is of such a shape that it cannot easily be cut with a power saw.

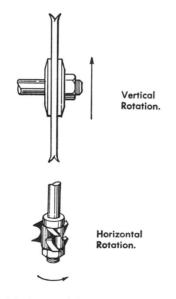

Vertical Rotation.

Horizontal Rotation.

Fig. 18:1   Methods of Cutting

There are three general types of shapers: heavy duty or production shapers; medium shapers, used in schools and small shops; and portable shapers or routers. All of these machines will perform more or less the same operations although not necessarily with the same efficiency, speed, and accuracy. Shapers are the most versatile of all woodworking machines. There is almost no end to the operations that can be performed on them through the use of jigs, templates, and the wide range of bits and cutters that are available.

Routers

Let us consider first the router, which is actually a portable shaper. The router is used in cabinet and furniture making for cutting edge mouldings of all types, for cutting channels for inlay work, for making dovetail joints, and for many other operations. Routers are used by carpenters for cutting hinge gains, for mortising locks, and for stair mortising.

The router consists of a high-speed motor with a collet-type chuck attached to the end of the shaft in which the cutters are held. This arrangement makes for a simple, efficient, direct-drive machine. The motor can be raised or lowered in the frame to determine the depth of the cut.

For quick, accurate depth setting, the router can be adjusted by turning the large calibrated ring that is threaded on the motor unit. The position of this ring determines the height of the motor in the frame. For finer adjustments a micrometer-type setting can be made

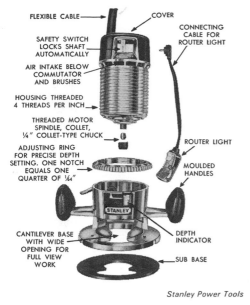

FLEXIBLE CABLE

COVER

CONNECTING CABLE FOR ROUTER LIGHT

SAFETY SWITCH LOCKS SHAFT AUTOMATICALLY

AIR INTAKE BELOW COMMUTATOR AND BRUSHES

HOUSING THREADED 4 THREADS PER INCH

THREADED MOTOR SPINDLE, COLLET, ¼" COLLET-TYPE CHUCK

ADJUSTING RING FOR PRECISE DEPTH SETTING. ONE NOTCH EQUALS ONE QUARTER OF ¹⁄₆₄"

ROUTER LIGHT

MOULDED HANDLES

CANTILEVER BASE WITH WIDE OPENING FOR FULL VIEW WORK

DEPTH INDICATOR

SUB BASE

Stanley Power Tools

Fig. 18:2   Parts of a Router

Stanley Power Tools

Fig. 18:3   Depth Setting

Porter-Cable

Fig. 18:4   Heavy Duty Router

(see Figure 18:3). A quick-action lock holds the motor at the required height setting.

Routers range in size and power from a light ¼ h.p. hobby size to the heavy duty 2½ h.p. production type used by building contractors and in woodworking plants. A heavy-duty router is shown in Figure 18:4.

Bits A to E, in Figure 18:5, are called one-piece bits because the shank and the cutter sections are forged out of one piece. The shaper cutters (G, H, I) have a hole in the centre and must be mounted on an arbor (F) between spacing collars in order to secure the desired cut. Most of the one-piece bits have a pilot below the cutter section that controls the horizontal depth of the cut by riding along the edge of the work. This edge must be finished smooth and to the correct shape before one of these bits is used.

Figure 18:6 illustrates a router with a bit with a pilot being used to put the moulded edge on a table top.

Router bits of the types shown in Figure 18:5 (A and B) have no pilot on the end of them as they are intended to cut a groove that is not at the edge of the work. When using this type of bit in a router you must use a guide. An adjustable guide, shown in Figure 18:7, is used for straight edges.

If the work is curved, as shown in Figure 18:8, a piece of wood can be cut to fit the contour of the work and attached to the guide.

If the groove is to be cut too far in from the edge for a guide to be attached

117

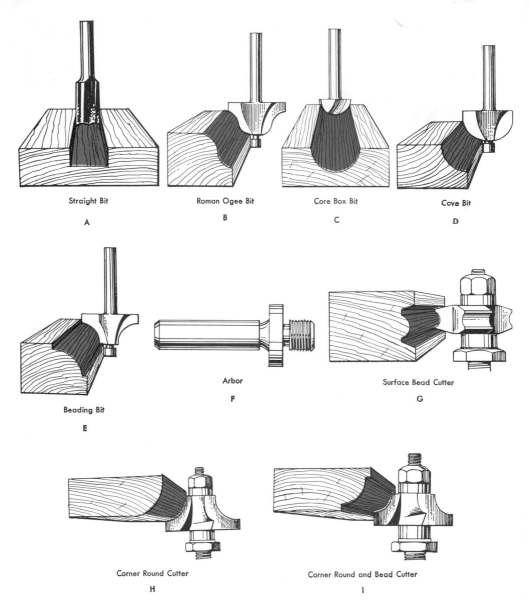

Straight Bit

A

Roman Ogee Bit

B

Core Box Bit

C

Cove Bit

D

Beading Bit

E

Arbor

F

Surface Bead Cutter

G

Corner Round Cutter

H

Corner Round and Bead Cutter

I

Fig. 18:5 Some of the Many Bits Available for the Router

to the router, a piece of scrap wood can be tacked or clamped to the face of the work to serve as a guide. For cutting rabbets in inside corners on such work as picture frames or window sashes, a block with a square corner can be fastened to the guide, as shown in Figure 18:9.

Circular grooves can be cut by using a trammel point guide arrangement, as shown in Figure 18:10. It has a sharp centre point that acts as a centre simi-

Porter-Cable

Fig. 18:6   Routing a Table Top

Stanley Power Tools

Fig. 18:7   Routing with a Guide

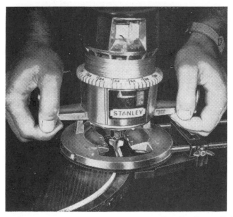

Stanley Power Tools

Fig. 18:8   Wood Section Added to Guide

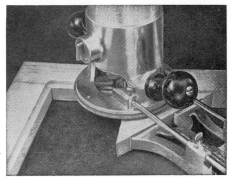

Stanley Power Tools

Fig. 18:9   Routing an Inside Corner

Stanley Power Tools

Fig. 18:10 Routing a Circle

lar to that of a pair of compasses. When the point is held in the wood, the router can be moved around it, forming a perfect circle.

Although it is best to use some type of pilot or guide for cutting with a router, it is possible to make most router cuts freehand; in fact, some cuts must be made this way. However, freehand cutting requires considerable skill and experience, and should not be attempted by the beginner.

Template routing

By using a straight router bit, and templates and template guides, duplicate pieces with irregular shapes or intricate designs can be cut quickly and accurately. A template is a pattern or guide

119

that is cut to the size and shape desired for the finished work, and eliminates the slowness and difficulty of cutting intricate designs freehand. The template guides the router over the work to cut the desired design. It may take a little time to make a good template, but once it is made, it can be used over and over again for routing any number of identical pieces.

Figure 18:11 shows some bits and a template guide. The guide is attached to the base of the router. The bit projects through the hole in the collar of the guide. The collar slides along the template. The template must be made slightly larger than the work to be cut to allow for the distance from the collar of the template guide to the cutting edge of the bit. No radius on the template should be smaller than that of the collar (see Figure 18:13).

Templates can easily be made from

Stanley Power Tools

Fig. 18:12 Template Layout

¼" plywood or hardboard. Simply lay out the design on paper and trace it onto the template material as shown in Figure 18:12. The shape can now be cut out on the jigsaw or freehand with the router. The edges should be well sanded to ensure a smooth guiding surface.

Clamp or tack the template to the work, as shown in Figure 18:13. Start the cut near the edge of the template, keeping the base of the router flat on the template and the collar of the guide against the edge. Let the router follow around the template until the pattern is entirely cut.

Metal templates are made for pro-

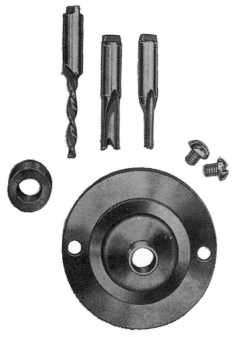

Stanley Power Tools

Fig. 18:11 Bits and Template Guide

Stanley Power Tools

Fig. 18:13 Use of Template

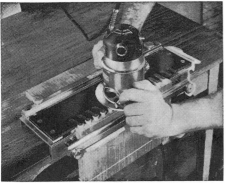

Porter-Cable

Fig. 18:14 Dovetail Template

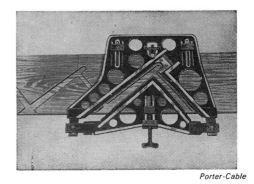

Porter-Cable

Fig. 18:16 Stair Template

duction operations in shops and for use by carpenters in the building trade. Figure 18:14 shows a template being used for the routing out of dovetail joints for cabinet drawer fronts. An adjustable butt hinge template is illustrated in Figure 18:15. This is used on either the door or the door frame. A great deal of time and effort can be saved by the carpenter through the use of the router in making the housed joints between the stair stringers and the treads and risers. An adjustable metal stair template is shown in Figure 18:16.

It is often more convenient to move the work than to pass the router over it, especially if the work is large. For this reason the router may be mounted under a table with the bit or cutter projecting through, as shown in Figures 18:17 and 18:18. The router motor unit can be tilted to 45°. Each degree that it is tilted produces a different shape with the same cutter.

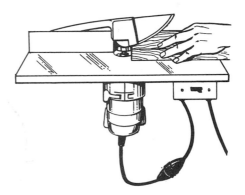

Fig. 18:17 Router and Table Attachment

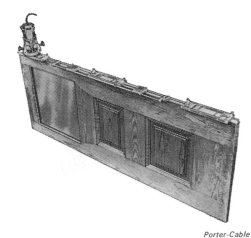

Porter-Cable

Fig. 18:15 Butt Hinge Template

Stanley Power Tools

Fig. 18:18 Table Guide

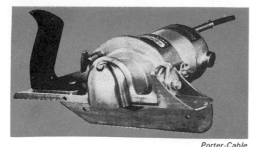

Porter-Cable

Fig. 18:19 Electric Plane Attachment

Fig. 18:21 Sharpening Attachment

The router motor unit may also be placed in a plane frame, thus making a portable electric plane. These planes are very useful for fitting doors and sash or planing the edge of any stock that is too large to plane conveniently on a jointer. A large jointer is not always available, especially in a new house where most of the doors and sash are fitted. A spiral-type cutter is used (see Figure 18:20). Because of the high speed of the router, a very smooth cut can be obtained.

Pointers on the use of a router

Since the router bits and cutters revolve in a clockwise direction, the router should be moved from left to right for straight cuts. When routing circular edges move the router in a counter-clockwise direction.

The speed at which the router is passed over the work depends on the size of the cut and the type of wood. If the router is moved too rapidly, it will overload the motor, causing the rpm to drop, and the result will be a rough cut. If the router is moved too slowly, the friction of the knife will burn the wood.

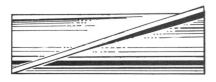

Fig. 18:20 Cutter Used in the Electric Plane

The router must be kept in motion at all times when routing edges, or serious burning will result from the high speed of the router knives. Most routers run at a speed of between 18,000 and 24,000 rpm.

When changing bits, make sure the round shank is inserted all the way into the chuck and tightened securely. For making smooth, even cuts the bits and cutters must be kept sharp. A special grinding wheel and grinding fixture can be used to sharpen the bits and cutters. The grinding wheel is rotated by the router, while the fixture holds the bit. This is shown in Figure 18:21.

Safety precautions for the router

Because the cutting tools of the router are exposed during its operation, the following precautions must be observed:

1. Keep your fingers well away from revolving bits and cutters.

2. Do not attempt to rout stock that is too small.

3. If the router is to be passed over the work, make sure the wood is clamped down.

4. Keep the base of the router flat on the surface of the work.

5. Hold the router firmly when you turn on the switch; this is necessary to overcome the starting torque of the motor.

122

6. Always disconnect the router before changing the cutters or bits.

7. Special care is needed when using the router in the inverted position with the cutter projecting through the table. In this position your hands are exposed to the cutter.

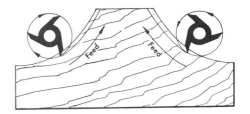

Fig. 18:23 The work should be fed into the grain and against the cutter.

Shapers

The *spindle shaper* consists of a frame, a power-driven vertical spindle projecting through the table top, a guide fence, a safety guard, and an assortment of cutters and collars.

Figure 18:22 shows a medium-sized shaper of the type that might be used in school and small woodworking shops. A larger production shaper is used in factories and mills.

In order to speed up production the shapers often used in industry have a double spindle. The spindles revolve in opposite directions, allowing the operator to feed the work from either the right or the left. This not only is easier for the operator, but also allows the work to be fed into the machine so that the cutters cut into the grain of the wood, making a much smoother cut with less chance of splintering. Figure 18:23 illustrates the direction in which the work should be fed.

The single spindle shaper shown in Figure 18:22 is often made with a reversing switch that changes the direction of rotation of the spindle.

There are two general types of cutters used on shapers: the *one-piece knife* type (Figure 18:24), which has three cutting lips, and the *open-faced knives* type, which has two individually ground blank knives (Figure 18:25). The one-piece cutters are used on smaller machines and are considered to be safer as there is no danger of their leaving the spindle while it is rotating. The

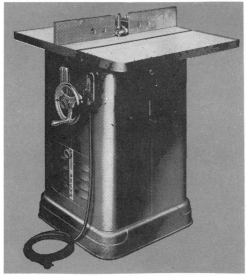

Delta Power Tool Div., Rockwell Mfg. Co.
Fig. 18:22 Medium-sized Shaper

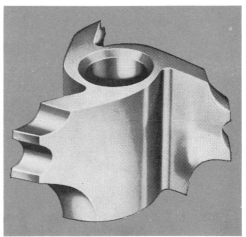

Delta Power Tool Div., Rockwell Mfg. Co.
Fig. 18:24 One-piece Cutter

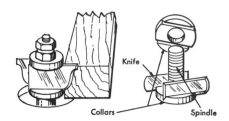

Fig. 18:25 Open-faced Knives

Fig. 18:26 Cutter Head with Three Knives

open-faced knives are more commonly used because they can so easily be ground to any desired shape. They fit between two slotted collars, which are held in place by a nut on the top of the spindle.

It is absolutely essential that the two knives be exactly the same width. If they are not, one will always be loose regardless of how tightly the nut is tightened. A loose cutter knife can cause serious injury if it flies out. The knives should be tested for width before they are used. This can be done by placing the knives in position and tightening the nut by hand. Grasp both knives and pull them outward simultaneously. If one knife slides more easily than the other, the knives are not matched and should not be used together.

Still another type of shaper knife is the *cutter head*, which has a solid centre section with three removable blades held firmly in place by Allen Screws (see Figure 18:26). These are used mainly as an attachment for a circular saw.

Operation of a shaper

There are several methods of guiding work against the shaper knives so that the desired shape is cut.

1. Hold the work to be cut against the shaper collar on the spindle and slide the work across the table.

2. When shaping straight work, hold it

firmly against the adjustable guide or fence.

3. Hold the stock to be shaped on a template, which, in turn, is held against the spindle collar.

4. Clamp the work on or against a jig or form, such as was described for the router earlier in this chapter. Whenever possible, use the fence to ensure safe operation. It will be noted that the depth of the cut can be regulated by moving the fence (see Figure 18:27).

Most shaping is done against a collar because it is so convenient to shape curved edges in this way. The work needs only to be held firmly against the collar, which will automatically control the depth of the cut if the knives are set correctly. The collar, knives, and work are shown in Figure 18:28.

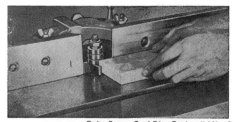

Fig. 18:27 Shaping with Work Against the Fence

Delta Power Tool Div., Rockwell Mfg. Co.

Fig. 18:28 Shaping with a Collar

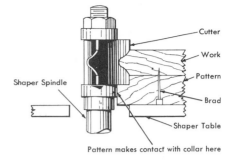

Pattern makes contact with collar here

Fig. 18:29

Industrial plants use patterns to advantage for shaping work to an exact size as they allow the entire edge of the work to be shaped. (This is not possible when the work must ride on the collar.) A pattern is cut to the exact size and the edges are finished smoothly. The work to be shaped is cut to rough size, i.e. 1/16" to 1/8" oversize. It is held to the pattern by anchor points, usually brads or nails driven through the pattern so that the points project, as shown in Figure 18:29. The template slides on the collar, making it possible to cut the full thickness of the work.

Safety precautions for the shaper

Of all the woodworking power machines the shaper is probably the most dangerous because it is impossible to keep the knives covered and because the work is fed into the machine by hand. For these reasons it is essential that you take every possible safety precaution when operating the shaper. The safety precautions listed for the router apply also to the shaper, as well as these additional ones:

1. Make sure the spindle nut is tight and that the knives are correctly adjusted before starting the shaper.

2. Use all guards and hold-down devices on the machine that will add to the safety of the operator. Figure 18:30 illustrates the hold-down arrangement on some shapers.

3. See that the spindle is free before turning on the machine. A lock is provided to secure the spindle while the nut is being tightened.

4. Keep your fingers as far away from the knives as the size of the work will permit.

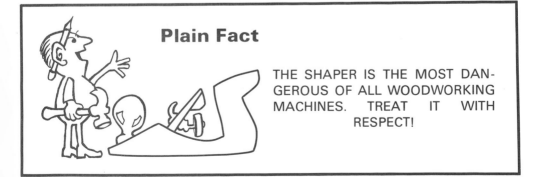

Plain Fact

THE SHAPER IS THE MOST DANGEROUS OF ALL WOODWORKING MACHINES. TREAT IT WITH RESPECT!

125

Delta Power Tool Div., Rockwell Mfg. Co.

Fig. 18:30 Safety Hold-down Arrangement

5. Do not attempt to shape small pieces unless they are held in a form or jig.

ASSIGNMENT

1. What is the difference between shaping and routing?

2. List three types of shapers.

Router

3. List four operations performed with the router by (a) cabinetmakers, (b) by carpenters.

4. How is the depth of the cut regulated?

5. What is the horsepower rating of a heavy-duty router?

6. Name and draw the shapes of four commonly used router bits.

7. What is the difference between a router bit and a router cutter?

8. Why do many router bits have a pilot pin below the cutting section?

9. Draw the shape of the part that must be cut and attached to the

guide to make the inlay cut in the table top shown below.

Cut to be made here for inlay

10. Why should a guide be used when cutting with a router?

11. What is the advantage of using templates for cutting parts to size with the router?

12. Explain how the template guide is used with the template in cutting work to size. You may use a drawing to clarify your answer.

13. For what operation do carpenters use router templates in home construction?

14. For what operation is an electric plane used?

15. Indicate with an arrow the direction in which the router should be moved when shaping the edge of the two pieces of stock shown here.

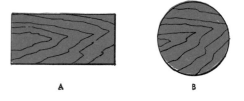

A   B

16. What would be the result if the router were moved too rapidly over the work? If it were moved too slowly?

17. List the three safety precautions that you consider most important when operating the router.

Shaper

18. What is the advantage of a double spindle shaper over a single spindle shaper?

19. Name the two general types of cutters used on the shaper. Which type is considered to be the safer?

20. (a) Why must shaper knives that are used in pairs have exactly the same width?
(b) Explain the method of testing the knives for proper width.

21. State the three methods of guiding the work against the shaper knives.

22. Explain how the collar on the spindle determines the depth of the shaper cut.

23. Explain how a template is used in cutting work to the correct size on the shaper.

24. Why is the shaper more dangerous than most other woodworking machines?

25. What is meant by the torque of a motor? (See Glossary of Terms.)

variety saws and radial arm saws

Variety saws

The *circular saw* is the most useful machine in any woodworking shop because of the time and labour it saves. Due to the large number of operations that can be performed on most circular saws, they are also called *variety saws*.

The size of a variety saw is determined by the diameter of the blade. The 8", 10", and 12" sizes are the ones most often used in woodworking shops.

There are two general types of variety saws: (a) the tilting table and (b) the tilting arbor or blade. In the first type the table is tilted for cutting angles, the blade remaining in one position. In the second type the table is stationary and the blade is tilted. The arbor is the power-driven shaft on which the blades are mounted. The tilting arbor or blade is generally considered to be the better saw. Some saws have a double arbor with two saw blades, one a rip saw, the other a cross-cut. Either saw can be turned up so it is above the table, while the other is below. A tilting arbor saw is shown in Figure 19:1.

Some of the many operations that can be performed on the variety saw are cross-cutting, ripping, bevelling, grooving, dadoing, and chamfering.

Types of blades commonly used are shown in Figure 19:2. Special carbide-tipped blades are made that are more

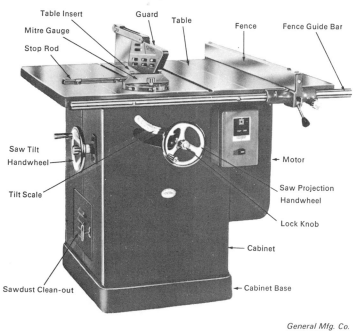

Table Insert Guard Table Fence Fence Guide Bar
Mitre Gauge
Stop Rod
Saw Tilt Handwheel
Tilt Scale
Motor
Saw Projection Handwheel
Lock Knob
Cabinet
Sawdust Clean-out
Cabinet Base

General Mfg. Co.

Fig. 19:1   Tilting Arbor Circular Saw

expensive but make a smoother cut and stay sharp longer than the all-steel conventional blades.

To cut easily and operate efficiently, saw blades must rotate at the correct speed. The larger the diameter of the blade, the greater the rim speed for a given rpm. Large production saws have large-diameter blades and a faster rim speed than the smaller bench saws. This allows the work to be fed faster and still produce a smooth cut. An 8" blade should rotate at 3400 rpm, giving it a rim speed of approximately 7100 feet per minute. A 10" blade should rotate at 3100 rpm, giving it a rim speed of approximately 8100 feet per minute, while a 12" blade (the size used in most school shops) generally rotates at 3400 rpm giving it a rim speed of approximately 10,000 feet per minute.

For most cutting operations the blade should be covered with a guard. When required, these guards can be easily removed or raised and swung to one side. However, this should only be done for operations that cannot be performed with the guard in place. All guards should have kick-back fingers to prevent the work from being thrown back at the operator. A basket-type guard with a splitter block is shown in Figure 19:3.

The rip saw guide, or *fence*, as it is usually called, is attached to the saw by means of bars at the front and back of the table. The front bar is calibrated in inches and fractions of an inch, so that the fence can be set for cutting to any desired width. There is a locking device to hold it permanently at any

Combination Blade.

Rip-saw Blade.

Cut-off or Cross-cut Blade.

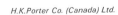
H.K.Porter Co. (Canada) Ltd.

Fig. 19:2 Types of Blades

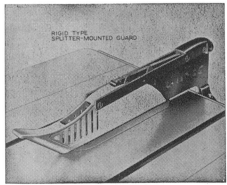

Delta Power Tool Div., Rockwell Mfg. Co.

Fig. 19:3 Saw Guard

129

Plain Fact

A CIRCULAR SAW CAN BE THE GREATEST OF ALL LABOUR-SAVING MACHINES BUT ALSO THE MOST DANGEROUS IF THE PROPER SAFETY PRECAUTIONS ARE NOT OBSERVED.

spot. The fence should be adjusted so that it is parallel with the saw blade, or the work will bind when being cut.

The cross-cut fence fits into the groove at the right or left side of the blade, making it possible to use the fence at either side of the blade. This fence on most saws can be tilted to cut at an angle, as shown in Figure 19:4. It is marked off in degrees so that it can be set at any angle. For this reason it is called a *mitre gauge*.

Adjustments

On a tilting arbor saw the blade is tilted to cut bevels by turning a hand wheel situated below the table. The degrees are marked on the tilt scale so that you can set and lock the blade at any desired angle. The height of the blade is adjusted by another hand wheel. The height of the blade will determine the depth of the cut for making dado or rabbet cuts.

Rip sawing

Ripping refers to cutting a board lengthwise. The face that rests on the saw table should be relatively flat and the edge to be placed against the rip saw fence should be straight to prevent binding or kick-backs.

A push stick must be used to guide the work through the saw. One such stick is shown in Figure 19:5. The part

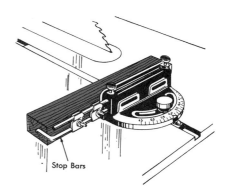

Stop Bars

Fig. 19:4 Mitre Gauge

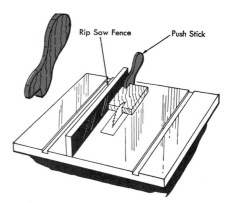

Rip Saw Fence   Push Stick

Fig. 19:5 Use of Rip Saw Fence and Push Stick (Guard left off for clarity)

of the board that you need should be between the fence and the saw. For instance, if you required a 2″ strip of wood to be cut from a piece 6″ wide, the fence should be set at the 2″ graduation on the front of the saw so that

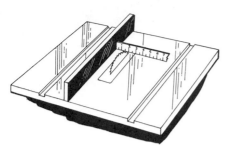

Fig. 19:6 Setting the Rip Saw Fence for Cutting to an Accurate Width

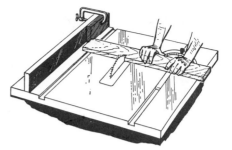

Fig. 19:7 Block Used as Length Guide (Guard left off for clarity)

the piece you want will be between the fence and the saw. If a very accurate width is desired, it is well to measure between the edge of the saw blade and the face of the fence, as is shown in Figure 19:6. If long stock is being ripped, the end must be supported, or a helper should assist you by guiding and supporting the piece as it comes through the saw. As a safety measure, do not stand directly behind the saw blade when rip sawing.

Cross-cut sawing

All cross-cutting must be done with the use of the cross-cut fence, more often called a mitre gauge. Never attempt to cut freehand without a guide.

When squaring the end of a piece of stock, move the rip saw fence well over out of the way. Now place the work against the cross-cut fence and hold it firmly while sliding both the fence and the work forward until the cut is made. Now draw the fence and stock back to the starting location. Leave the waste stock on the saw table. When cutting several pieces to the same length, you may use the rip saw fence as a length guide if a block is clamped to it at a point just ahead of the blade (see Figure 19:7). Never use the rip saw fence itself as the length guide. The piece that is cut off may bind between the fence and the blade and be thrown back at the operator.

Other cutting operations

Rip sawing and cross-cutting are referred to as straight-line cutting operations. There are a great number of other more intricate cutting operations that can be performed on the variety saw. These you will become familiar with as you gain experience in using the saw.

Two of the attachments used for some of these operations are the dado head and the moulding head. The dado head consists of two saw blades and several cutters ranging in thickness from ⅛" to ¼". This arrangement of blades and cutters can be assembled to cut grooves from ¼" to ⅞" in width.

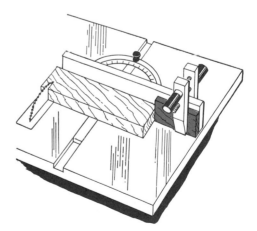

Fig. 19:8 Length Stop Attached to the Cross-cut Fence

131

Delta Power Tool Div., Rockwell Mfg. Co.

Fig. 19:9 Dado Head Blades and Cutters

The regular saw blade is removed and the dado head blades and cutters are put on the arbor in its place. Allow the dado head to project above the table the desired depth of the groove to be cut. This arrangement is very handy for cutting dadoes or recesses in the upright parts of cupboards to support the shelving, as well as for many other jobs. The dado head blades and cutters are shown in Figure 19:9.

The moulding head is used for cutting shaped mouldings of many types, such as those used on window sash and table tops. This attachment consists of the head and three interchangeable knives, which are locked in place by Allen Screws. A large number of knives may be obtained in different shapes. They are made in sets of three, ground exactly alike. See Figure 19:10 for some of these shapes.

The moulding head is put on the arbor in place of the blade with the knives projecting sufficiently above the table to make the moulded cut on the edge of the work.

Safety precautions for the variety saw

Power saws are responsible for a larger number of serious accidents than any other woodworking machine. It is therefore essential that you know as much as possible about saws. Be on the alert and exercise all possible safety precautions. Points you should remember:

1. Use the guard for all operations except those which cannot be performed with it in place. In such cases extra care must be taken.

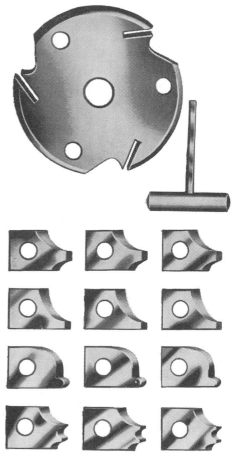

Delta Power Tool Div., Rockwell Mfg. Co.

Fig. 19:10 Moulding Head and Knives

2. Do not stand directly behind the saw blade.

3. Do not reach over the saw blade with your hand. Keep your hands well away from the revolving blade at all times.

4. Always use a push stick when rip sawing.

5. When rip sawing make sure the edge of the piece placed against the rip saw fence is straight.

6. When cross-cutting do not place the end of the piece against the rip saw fence.

7. Always use either the rip or the cross-cut fence; never attempt to cut freehand.

8. Do not clean, adjust, or oil the saw while the blade is in motion.

9. Never attempt to cut pieces less than 8" long.

10. If you are in doubt about the set-up or operation of the saw, ask your instructor for help.

The observance of these rules is a matter of common sense and respect for a useful and powerful machine that can be dangerous if not properly used.

Radial arm saws

The radial arm saw shown in Figure 19:11 is a relatively new type of power

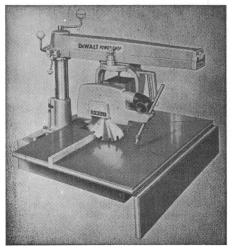

DeWalt Power Tools

Fig. 19:11 Radial Arm Saw

saw. It was developed from the older-type swing saw used by lumber yards and mills. The radial saw differs from the variety saw in that for most operations the work remains stationary while the saw blade is moved. The saw blade is attached directly to the motor shaft. A higher-speed universal motor is used that travels at 6500 rpm, faster than most variety saws. This enables it to operate more efficiently with the router head and other attachments.

The principle of the radial arm saw is that the motor and saw blade are mounted on a movable overhead arm. A Y-shaped yoke attaches the motor unit to the arm.

Plain Fact

THINK SAFETY FIRST AND THE OPERATION OF THE SAW SECOND.

The three hinge points at the arm, yoke, and motor unit can be likened to the human arm, elbow, and wrist, which allow the hand to be placed in any position within the circle of the arm. The shoulder action is shown in Figure 19:12. The arm of the saw will swing on the column through the full circle. The elbow movement is illustrated in Figure 19:13. The yoke will swing a full 90° in either direction and lock in position for ripping. Figure 19:14 shows the wrist action of the motor, which can be tilted to any angle for bevel cuts. The motor can also be set vertically, placing the blade in a horizontal position. The arm can be raised or lowered for different depths of cut, as shown in Figure 19:15.

These three points of adjustment allow the blade to be placed in any position, angle, or height over the saw table. This fact makes the radial arm saw a very efficient and versatile machine.

Some of the basic operations performed on this saw are cross-cutting, rip sawing, bevelling, and mitring, as well as the making of combination cuts (sometimes called *compound cuts*). Moulding, dadoing, sanding, drilling, and shaping can be done on this machine by using special attachments.

One of the advantages of any overhead power saw is that the cutting action is in full view of the operator at all times.

Safety precautions for the radial arm saw

The safety precautions to be observed while operating the radial arm saw are the same as those for the variety saw

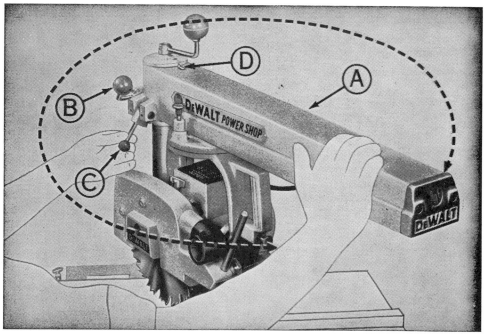

DeWalt Power Tools

Fig. 19:12 To rotate arm — Release arm clamp handle (B) and lift mitre latch (C). Then swing the arm (A) into the desired angle to either the right or the left. The mitre scale marked off in degrees is shown at (D).

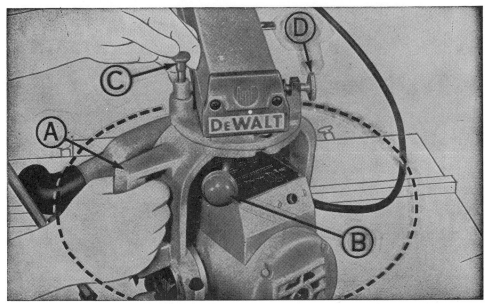

DeWalt Power Tools

Fig. 19:13 To swivel the saw on the arm — Release swivel clamp (B) and lift locating pin (C). Now swing the yoke (A) to the desired angle to the right or the left, and lock it in place by tightening the clamp (D).

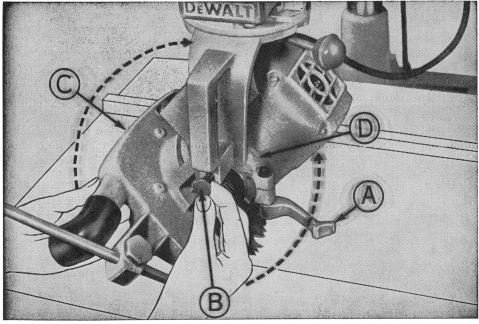

DeWalt Power Tools

Fig. 19:14 To tilt the saw for bevel cuts — Raise the arm until the saw is well above the table. Pull out the bevel clamp (A) and the locating pin (B). Tilt the motor (C) to any desired angle on the bevel scale (D) and relock clamp (A).

DeWalt Power Tools

Fig. 19:15 To raise or lower the saw — Turn the elevation handle (A). One revolution of the handle moves the saw ⅛″. Cut on the pull stroke when cross-cutting. (Note: The illustrations shown in Figures 19:12 to 19:15 are all of one make of saw. However, most other makes operate on the same principle and have similar adjustments.)

with the following additional points:

1. There is a lock for each adjustment. These must all be tight before starting the saw.

2. For cross-cutting or angle cutting, have the motor fully back against the column when positioning the work or starting the cut.

3. The saw blade rotates clockwise or toward the column. You should therefore cut on the pull stroke. The rotation of the saw helps to keep the work tight against the guide.

4. Keep in mind the direction of rotation when mounting saw blades or attachments.

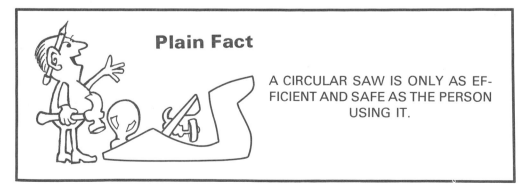

Plain Fact

A CIRCULAR SAW IS ONLY AS EFFICIENT AND SAFE AS THE PERSON USING IT.

5. When rip sawing, make sure you enter the wood from the right side of the saw. Most saws have an arrow indicating the correct direction.

6. Have the anti-kick-back fingers resting on the wood when rip sawing.

7. Mount all attachments and accessories according to the saw manufacturer's instructions.

ASSIGNMENT

Variety saw

1. Why are many circular saws called variety saws?

2. How is the size of a variety saw determined?

3. State the difference between a tilting table and a tilting arbor variety saw.

4. List five operations that can be performed on the variety saw.

5. What are the four types of blades used on a variety saw?

6. What would be the rim speed of a 12" saw blade if the rpm is 3000?

7. What is the purpose of the kickback fingers on the saw guards?

8. On a saw, what is the rip or crosscut guide called?

9. Why is the cross-cut saw fence called a mitre gauge?

10. Why should the part of the wood you require lie between the fence and the saw blade when ripping?

11. If you wish to cut 6" off the end of a 3' board, how would you set up

and operate the saw (in relation to the mitre gauge and rip saw fences)?

12. If each of the saw blades used on a dado head is ⅛" thick, what thickness of cutters would be required between them to cut a dado ⅞" wide?

13. List: (a) One important safety rule that must be followed when crosscutting. (b) One safety rule for rip sawing. (c) Three general safety rules required when any type of blade is used.

14. Explain the use of a splitter block (see Glossary of Terms).

Radial arm saw

15. Explain the chief difference between a radial arm saw and a variety saw.

16. What is the principle of the cutting action of the radial arm saw?

17. What are the three major adjustments on a radial saw?

18. What is a compound cut?

19. List some of the operations that can be performed on the radial saw through the use of attachments.

20. List three important safety precautions that apply specifically to the radial arm saw.

21. If the blade of a radial arm saw revolves at 6500 rpm, what would be the rim speed of a 12" blade?

22. Explain how you would set up a radial arm saw to cut a compound angle.

CHAPTER TWENTY

planing machines

Jointer

The two machines used to plane smooth and true surfaces and edges on lumber are the jointer and the planer. Of these two machines the more versatile is the jointer because it can be used for planing both the broad surfaces and the edges of stock, as well as for bevelling, tapering, and rabbeting.

The sequence of operations for planing stock with a machine is the same as that used for planing stock by hand. The first step should be to plane the best surface flat and smooth. This can be done most efficiently on the jointer. The jointer may also be used to reduce stock to any desired thickness, although under ordinary conditions a planer is used for this purpose.

The size of the jointer is determined by the length of the cylinder. Jointers range in size from 4" to 36". A 16" jointer is shown in Figure 20:1.

The wood is planed off the lower side of the board by passing it over a rapidly revolving cylinder on which are mounted two or more knives. The cylinder and its cutter knives make up the *cutter head*. The thickness of the cut is governed by the height of the *infeed table*. This is the front table or the part over which the wood is started. The *outfeed table* is the opposite end of the machine on which the planed part of the wood rests. The outfeed table should be exactly the same height as the highest point of the arc described by the revolving knives on the cylinder.

The infeed table should be set below the outfeed table a distance equal to the required cut. The lower the infeed table is set, the heavier will be the cut. The amount of wood to be removed at one cut will depend on the following factors:

(a) *The width of the piece*. The wider the board, the smaller the cut should be.

(b) *The type of wood*. A lighter cut must be made on hardwood than on softwood.

Fig. 20:1   16" Jointer

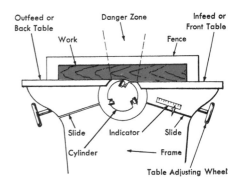

Fig. 20:2   Cutting Action of a Jointer

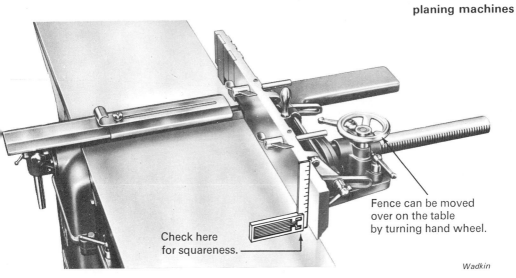

Check here
for squareness. ─┘

Fence can be moved
over on the table
by turning hand wheel.

Wadkin

Fig. 20:3

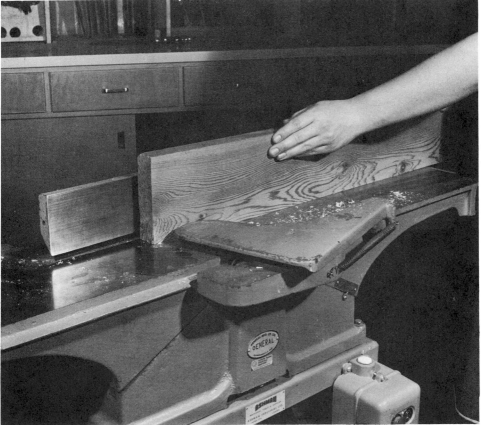

James C. Fish Photography

Fig. 20:4   Jointer with Spring Guard

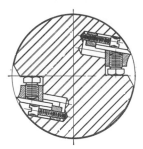

Standard Two-knife Wedge Type Cutterblock.

Section Through Standard Two-knife Wedge Type Cutterblock.

Wadkin

Fig. 20:5

(c) The smoothness of the finish. If you wish only to reduce the thickness of a piece of stock, larger cuts can be taken than when making a cut to produce a fine finish.

In general, a ⅛" cut may be made on the edge of a 1" piece and a ¹/₁₆" cut from the face side of a piece of 1" ×6" stock. This adjustment is made by turning the hand wheel on the front of the jointer.

A graduated scale and an indicating arrow is provided on most machines. The height of the outfeed table should be adjusted *only* when the knives have been changed or sharpened.

When planing the edge of a piece of stock, you should hold the side firmly against the fence. If an angle is to be cut, the fence can be tilted. If the piece is being jointed for an edge-to-edge joint, make sure the fence is set exactly at a 90° angle to the table. It is well to check it with a try square, as shown in Figure 20:3.

When planing the face of a warped board, place the cupped side down, as shown in Figure 20:6. After this side has been planed on the jointer, it can be brought to thickness on the planer. If it is to be reduced to thickness on the jointer, the thickness must be scribed on it with a marking gauge. It is pos-

sible to plane it down to thickness on the jointer if you pay close attention to the scribed line. Feed the work into the jointer so that the knives will cut with the grain of the wood.

One of the main uses of the jointer is to remove the twist from a piece of stock (that is, a piece that is slightly propeller-shaped). One face can be trued up on the jointer. Then the piece can be brought to thickness on the planer from the true face.

To cut tapers, first square a line across the work at the point where the taper starts. Lower the work onto the table with the line over the centre of the cylinder and set the height of the infeed table to the amount of taper required.

To cut stop chamfers, clamp blocks to the fence at the required locations so that the chamfer starts and stops at the right spot.

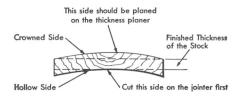

Fig. 20:6 Planing a Warped Board

Safety precautions for the jointer

Although the jointer is not a difficult machine to operate, it has been responsible for many serious accidents, most of them due to carelessness or lack of knowledge on the part of the operator.

The following are some of the safety precautions that must be observed while operating the jointer:

1. The guard must be in place at all times (over the knives and against the work). Two types of guard are shown in Figures 20:3 and 20:4. Many machines are equipped with a spring-loaded guard that presses tightly against the work as it is being cut, and then snaps back to the fence after the work has passed the cylinder. This type is considered superior to the type that must be set for each width of board.

2. When planing the face side of a piece of stock, a push stick should be used. This keeps the hands well away from the knives. A handy push stick that you can make is shown in Figure 20:7.

3. It is not always possible to use a push stick. In these cases keep your fingers well away from the ends of the piece. Do not allow your hands to rest on the part of the stock that is directly over the cutter head. This is referred to as the *danger zone* (see Figure 20:3).

4. Do not plane stock shorter than 10" or thinner than ⅝"

5. Do not adjust the fence or clean the shavings from the table while the cutter head is in motion.

6. Observe the amount of wood the jointer is set to cut before turning on the machine. It is well to make a trial cut on a scrap piece of wood.

7. Do not plane end grain unless the board is at least 11" wide.

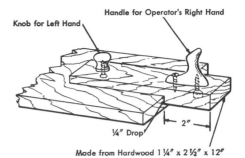

Knob for Left Hand — Handle for Operator's Right Hand

¼" Drop — 2"

Made from Hardwood 1 ¼" x 2 ½" x 12"

Fig. 20:7 Push Stick

Surface planer

The planer in many respects is similar to the jointer in that one surface of the work is planed by the knives on a rotating cylinder. The planer differs, however, in that it planes the upper surface of the wood. Its only uses are to plane the surface of the stock and to reduce it to the correct thickness.

The capacity of most *single surface planers* is from ¼" to 9" in thickness and 20", 24", and 36" in width, although larger planers are made for special purposes.

A single surface planer, sometimes called a *thickness planer*, is shown in Figure 20:8. This is the type to be found in most schools and small shops.

Wadkin

Fig. 20:8 Panel Planer

141

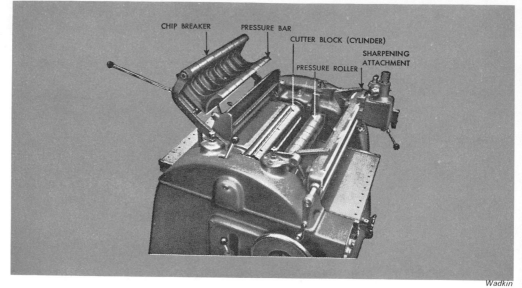

CHIP BREAKER   PRESSURE BAR

CUTTER BLOCK (CYLINDER)

SHARPENING ATTACHMENT

PRESSURE ROLLER

Wadkin

Fig. 20:9 Chip Breaker Swung Up To Expose Cutter Block and Pressure Roller

Double surface planers are made that have two cutter heads and plane both the top and bottom surface of the wood in one operation.

The planer operates basically in this way. The wood is drawn into the machine by a corrugated power-driven roller at the infeed end. The stock passes under a spring-loaded pressure bar and chip breaker. The former holds the work down firmly while the revolving cylinder knives remove the surface of the wood, after which it passes under a smooth roller on the outfeed end of the machine. There are also two smooth rollers on the bottom table that help to draw the wood through the planer.

The pressure or infeed roller and the pressure bar are both made in individual spring-loaded sections to take care of any roughness or raised section in the surface of the rough lumber that might otherwise cause it to stick. The springs allow a small section of the roller or bar to spring up and the wood to pass through the planer.

Most planers have two motors. One operates the cutting head while the other operates the feed rollers. This allows the feed rollers to work independently of the cylinder and makes it possible to have three or four different roller speeds. The speed of the cylinder, however, does not change. An efficient cutting-head speed is 5000 rpm. There are generally four knives inserted in the cylinder. Most planers are equipped with a sharpening device whereby the knives are sharpened while they are mounted in the planer.

The table is raised or lowered by a

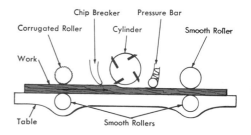

Chip Breaker   Pressure Bar

Corrugated Roller   Cylinder   Smooth Roller

Work

Table   Smooth Rollers

Fig. 20:10 Operation of the Planer

142

hand wheel on the side of the planer. A scale and pointer indicates the thickness to which the piece will be cut.

The amount of wood to be cut off at one time will depend on the width of the piece and the hardness of the wood, but, in general, a ⅛" cut may be made on softwood and ¹/₁₆" cut on hardwoods. Generally one revolution of the hand wheel raises the table ⅛".

How to set and operate a planer

1. Set the planer to cut ¹/₁₆" less than the thickness of the piece. If several pieces are to be planed at once, set it for the thickest piece.

2. Before feeding the wood, note the direction of the grain. With a planer, as with a hand plane, the wood must be cut with the grain. The point of the grain should be toward the operator. The cylinder rotates in the opposite direction to the feed rollers. Figure 20:11 illustrates which end of the board should enter the planer first.

3. If the pieces are more than 4" wide, put only one piece through at a time.

4. When several pieces are being planed at a time, put all the pieces through before resetting the thickness for the next cut.

5. If the piece is badly warped or twisted, a true surface should be cut

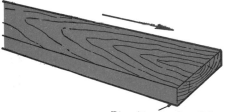

This end to enter planer first

Fig. 20:11

on the jointer. This face can then be placed down on the table so that the rough side may be planed parallel to it. If, however, the boards are reasonably straight and true, both sides may be planed on the planer, in which case an equal amount should be cut off each side. If a warped board is planed on the planer, the rollers will hold it down while it is being planed, but when it leaves the machine it will have the same warped or twisted shape.

Safety precautions for the planer

Although the planer is probably the safest of the woodworking machines because there are no exposed knives or blades, there are still, however, several limitations and safety precautions that must be observed.

1. Do not plane boards that are less than 14" long. If a piece passes completely under the infeed roller before it reaches the outfeed roller, it will stay in the machine until it is cut smaller by the revolving knives. Then it may be thrown back at the operator, causing injury.

2. Do not attempt to plane stock less than ¼" thick.

3. Make sure the pieces are free from nails or other foreign matter that might seriously damage the blades. If the lumber has pitch on the surface, be especially careful not to lay rules or other small tools on it as they may be drawn into the machine.

4. Do not place your hands near the infeed rollers. Under no circumstances should you reach into the machine when it is in operation.

5. Let the machine reach full speed before inserting the stock.

ASSIGNMENT

Jointer

1. List five operations that can be performed on the jointer.
2. Does the cutter head revolve toward the infeed or the outfeed table?
3. What governs the depth of the cut on a jointer?
4. What should be the height of the outfeed table in relation to the cutting knives?
5. What factors will determine the amount of wood to be removed for each cut?
6. Should a larger cut be taken off the face or off the edge of a board?
7. In general, how much wood should be taken off the piece in one cut?
8. Describe the operation of bringing a piece of work to a given thickness on the jointer.
9. Explain how to cut a taper on the jointer.
10. How and why is a push stick used?
11. List the four safety precautions that you consider the most important in the operation of a jointer.

Planer

12. What is the difference between a single surface planer and a double surface planer?
13. What causes the board to be drawn through the planer?
14. Which surface of the wood is planed as it passes through the planer?
15. What is a suitable amount of material to be removed from hardwood in one cut?
16. Why is the infeed roller made in spring-loaded sections?
17. When planing a group of boards to thickness, should you set the planer to cut the thinnest or the thickest piece?
18. Why should one face of a twisted board be planed on the jointer before it is cut to thickness on the planer?
19. Why should short stock never be cut on the planer?
20. How can you develop confidence when operating woodworking machines?

fasteners and hardware

Fasteners

The use and the application of hardware and various types of fastening devices is an interesting and important part of woodwork. Most projects you will be called upon to make will require one or more pieces of hardware or special fasteners.

Let us consider some of the fastening devices other than nails and screws. The threaded *machine screw* with either round or flat head is a strong and useful method of attaching two or more pieces of wood together and is used where a great deal of strength is required.

The *carriage bolt* is often used in wood. It has a round head and a square section below it that prevents the bolt from turning when the nut is tightened. The oval head can be drawn neatly into the wood with only the top exposed. These bolts come in a wide range of

sizes from ¼" to ¾" in diameter and from 1" to 12" in length.

The *stove bolt* is a loosely used term referring to small, threaded bolts with either flat or round slotted heads. They range in size from $5/32$" to ⅜" in diameter and up to 6" in length. They are used mainly for the application of hardware to wood. Figure 21:2 shows a flat-head stove bolt and a round-head one.

The *lag screw* may be classed as either a bolt or a wood screw. It has a square head and must be turned with a wrench, but it has a tapered thread like a wood screw. It is not used with a nut, but depends for its holding power on the fact that it is threaded into the wood just as a wood screw is. The proper-sized pilot hole must be drilled to

Fig. 21:3 Lag Screw

Fig. 21:1 Carriage Bolt

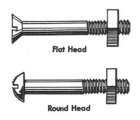

Flat Head

Round Head

Fig. 21:2 Stove Bolts

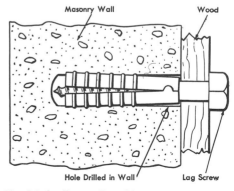

Masonry Wall   Wood

Hole Drilled in Wall   Lag Screw

Fig. 21:4 Expanding Shield

accommodate the threaded part. If it is used to fasten wood to a masonry surface, an expanding shield must be used, as in Figure 21:4. A hole is drilled in the masonry wall with a star drill (see Figure 21:5). The shield should fit snugly into the hole until the end is flush with the face of the wall. The lag screw can then be threaded into the shield, causing it to expand and tighten in the wall. A different-sized shield must be used for each size of lag screw. Smaller shields can be used for wood screws. *Tampins* are special shields that are threaded for machine screws. Many other types of fastening devices are on the market for attaching screws and bolts of all sizes to masonry walls but they all work on the same principle of an expanding fibre or metal sleeve that is inserted in the wall with the fastener threading into it.

Toggle bolts are used to attach wood strips or metal hardware to a hollow plastered wall. A wing nut with a pivot arm is used that can be folded and inserted through the hole, where it will automatically tilt down and provide a support against the lath or plaster base. The bolt is tightened from the outside with a screwdriver (see Figure 21:7).

Another type of patented fastener used on plastered walls is shown in Figure 21:8. It consists of an upset rivet, a bolt sleeve, and a double hex nut. A small hole is drilled through the plaster, and the sleeve is inserted and tightened with a wrench.

Corrugated fasteners are a common device used as a quick and easy method of holding two pieces of wood together edge to edge or end to edge. They are often used in conjunction with nails, glue, or wood screws on such things as picture frames and window screens. They should not be used for fine work but they have their place in more or less rough or temporary work. Many staple-type fasteners are available for similar purposes.

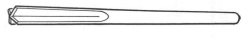

Fig. 21:5   Star Drill. Rotate the drill as it is tapped with a hammer.

Stanley Tools

Fig. 21:6   Carbide-tipped Masonry Drill for Drilling Holes in Masonry Walls with a Power Drill

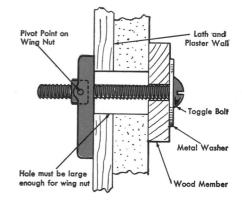

Pivot Point on Wing Nut

Lath and Plaster Wall

Toggle Bolt

Metal Washer

Hole must be large enough for wing nut

Wood Member

Fig. 21:7   Toggle Bolt

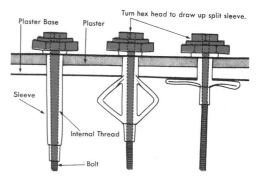

Turn hex head to draw up split sleeve.

Plaster Base   Plaster

Sleeve

Internal Thread

Bolt

Fig. 21:8   Stages in Action of a Clamp-up Fastener in a Hollow Plastered Wall

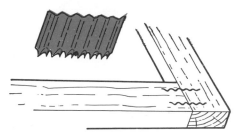

Fig. 21:9 Corrugated Fasteners

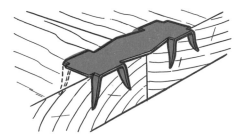

Fig. 21:10 Skotch Fastener

Hardware

Hinges

Figure 21:11 shows a standard *butt hinge*, which consists of two separate hinge leaves and a hinge pin.

Butt hinges are made in many sizes. Some have loose pins, while others have solid pins that are not removable. These are the cheaper variety that are often mounted on the surface with the entire hinge exposed. There is a stand-

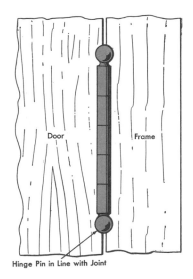

Fig. 21:12

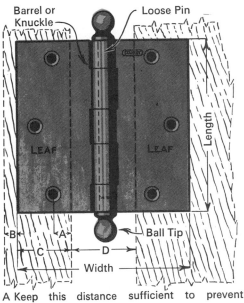

A Keep this distance sufficient to prevent splitting.

B Set back enough to prevent splitting when chiseling.

C Width of gain.

D Maximum clearance when door is open.

Stanley Tools

Fig. 21:11 Butt Hinge

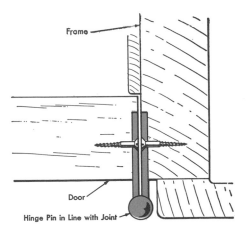

Fig. 21:13

147

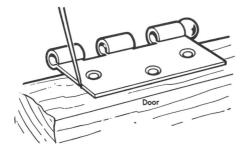

Fig. 21:14 Marking Hinge Location

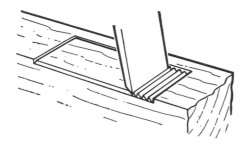

Fig. 21:15 Cutting Out Hinge Gain

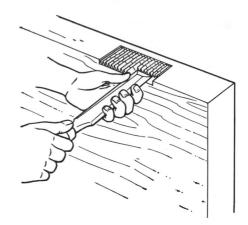

Fig. 21:16 Removing Stock from Hinge Gain with Paring Chisel

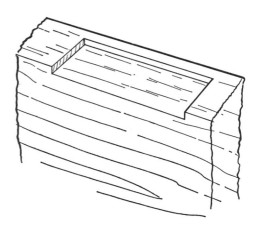
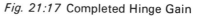

Fig. 21:17 Completed Hinge Gain

ard procedure in mounting loose pin hinges to doors and door frames. This operation is referred to as *hanging a door*, whether it be a large one or a small one. A groove must be cut in the door and the frame for the individual hinge leaves. These are called *hinge gains*. They are cut by locating the hinge in its correct location and scribing round the leaf with a knife or a pencil. Cut around this outline with a chisel; then make several cuts as shown in Figure 21:15. The wood can then be easily pared out and the hinge leaf screwed in place. One-half the hinge is attached to the door, then the door should be placed in the opening and wedged into position for the correct clearance at the top, the bottom, and the sides. The hinge locations can now be marked on the door frame. After removing the door you can then recess the second half of the hinge into the frame in the same manner as in the door. The door can then be replaced in the opening and the hinge pins set in place.

Butt hinges are made from steel, brass, or bronze and in various finishes such as chrome or nickel plate.

Time can be saved in laying out the hinge gains by using a *butt gauge*. This tool has two adjustable marking pins. One is set to mark the thickness of the hinge leaf, the other the width of the leaf. It is used as shown in Figure 21:19.

Some of the other types of hinges commonly used are shown in Figures 21:20-21:23. Most of these hinges can be considered as *surface hinges*, which, unlike the butt hinges, are mounted

Stanley Tools

Fig. 21:18 Butt Gauge

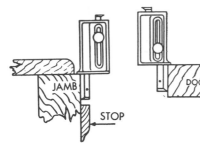

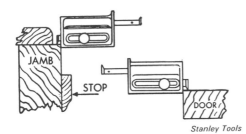

Stanley Tools

Fig. 21:19 How To Use a Butt Gauge

Fig. 21:20 T Hinge

Fig. 21:21 Strap Hinge

Fig. 21:22 Butterfly Hinge

Fig. 21:23 Ornamental Surface Hinge

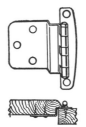

Fig. 21:24 Semi-concealed Offset Cabinet Door Hinge

directly on the surface with all the hinge exposed. This type is easier to install. Although each type of hinge requires a different treatment for its installation, they are all based on a careful spacing and alignment. The centre of the hinge pin must be directly opposite and parallel with the joint between the door and the frame, as shown in Figure 21:12, if the door is to operate smoothly without binding or sticking.

The *offset hinge* (Figure 21:24) is one that is much used for kitchen cabinet work. It is made to fit the lipped plywood doors so extensively used in modern cupboards. One-half the hinge is attached to the back of the door, the other half to the door trim. These hinges have solid pins and may be purchased in wrought iron, chrome, nickel, or copper finishes.

149

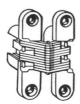

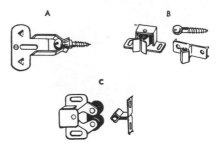

Fig. 21:25 Totally Concealed Cabinet Door Hinge

Fig. 21:27 Friction Catches

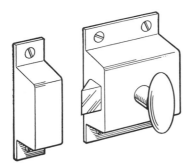

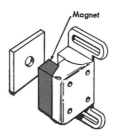

Fig. 21:26 Surface Catch

Fig. 21:28 Magnetic Catch

Catches

To keep the door closed, a wide range of styles of door catches is made to go with the hinges just described. Generally speaking, the style of catch and handle should match the hinges used. On small doors the handle is generally referred to as the door pull.

There are two main types of door catch:

1. *Surface catches* are those that are attached to the face of the door and have a knob that is turned to release the latch and also to act as a pull (see Figure 21:26).

2. *Friction catches* are the more popular type. They are attached to the back of the door. There are many variations of this catch. Some work with small coil springs, others with thin, flat steel stock, but all operate on the same principle. The small section is mounted on the door and the larger

spring section on the underside of a shelf or to the side of the door jamb. The spring action of the one part fitting inside the other holds the door securely closed but allows the door to be opened with the door pull. These catches require careful alignment on installation if they are to operate well. Friction catches are illustrated in Figure 21:27.

The *magnetic catch* is now frequently used. It consists of two small magnets, one on each section of the catch. When the door is closed and the magnets make contact, the door is held firmly shut.

Locks

For small doors that require a lock, a *mortise cabinet lock* or *chest lock* may be used. They are equally useful for drawers or doors. They are either mortised into or mounted on the inside of the door or drawer. A keeper plate must

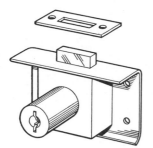

Fig. 21:29 Mortise Cabinet Lock

be set into the frame to receive the lock bolt as shown in Figure 21:29.

Pulls

Door and drawer pulls may be made of metal, wood, glass, or plastic. Most of these are attached by one or two

screws drilled through from the back of the door, as shown in Figure 21:31.

For this hardware to look well and serve the purpose for which it was intended, it must be applied properly and with care. All screws should be driven straight and the correct size screwdriver must be used so as not to burr the slots on the screw heads. A pilot hole should be made for the screws. For this it is best to use a screw set, a convenient tool that enables the pilot hole to be located exactly in the centre of a screw hole in the hardware and the wood screw to be properly aligned with the hole (see Figure 21:32).

Some other kinds of hardware, often used in general woodwork, are shown in Figures 21:33 to 21:35.

Fig. 21:30 Metal Drawer Pull

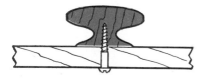

Fig. 21:31 Wood Knob Pull

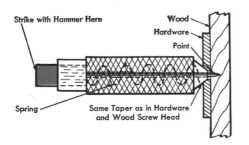

Strike with Hammer Here — Wood — Hardware — Point — Spring — Same Taper as in Hardware and Wood Screw Head

Fig. 21:32 Screw Set

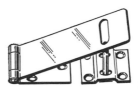

Fig. 21:33 Hasp

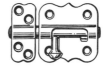

Fig. 21:34 Barrel Bolt

Fig. 21:35 Steel Corner Brace

ASSIGNMENT

Fasteners

1. What are the distinguishing features of a carriage bolt?

2. Why are carriage bolts used much more in wood than in metal?

3. In what way is a lag screw similar to a wood screw? In what ways does it differ?

4. Explain how a piece of wood can be fastened to a masonry wall with lag screws and shields.

5. Where and for what purpose are toggle bolts used?

6. Why should corrugated fasteners not be used for fine work?

Hardware

7. List the steps in hanging a door, using butt hinges.

8. Make drawings of three other types of hinges and list one place where you think each might be used.

9. Explain the difference between a surface catch and a friction catch.

10. What is the handle of a small door called?

11. What should be the main consideration in installing any hinge?

12. How does a magnetic catch operate?

13. Why is it important that the screws be driven straight? How is the screw set used to accomplish this?

14. Describe a type of catch or door pull you have seen that has not been described here.

CHAPTER TWENTY-TWO

wood joints

The construction of good joints is an important part of woodwork. Very few objects of wood can be made from one single piece. We do not consider two pieces of wood that have simply been nailed or screwed together as forming a wood joint in the true sense. However, when two pieces are cut or shaped to fit each other so that with the aid of glue they are as strong as, or stronger than, one single piece and have a neat appearance, they can be considered to make a good wood joint. There are a great number of joints used in all branches of the woodworking trade; only the ones most frequently used are described here.

Edge-to-edge joint

One of the joints you may be called upon to make first is the edge-to-edge joint. This joint is used when making many articles of wood that require parts wider than one piece of lumber. This makes it necessary to glue two or more boards edge to edge to make one wide section. It is seldom possible to get a board wide enough for the larger sections of most furniture; even if it were, it is more advisable to make the part by gluing narrow boards together, as it will keep its shape better. Lumber more than 6" wide should not be used for good cabinetmaking, as the wider the piece the greater the warpage that will take place. It is important that warpage be kept to a minimum. One of the ways this can be done is to use narrow stock.

In preparing the pieces for gluing, you must take several factors into consideration:

1. The grain of the wood should run in the same direction in each piece.

2. Place the face side of all boards up; the better of the two sides should be considered the face. Mark this side with the letter *F* or some other indicating check mark.

3. Try to position the pieces so that their colour, grain, and texture match.

4. Reverse the direction of the annual ring on alternate boards.

Lumber tends to warp in the direction of the annual rings. That is, the rings tend to straighten out, warping the piece into a cup shape. This warpage can be reduced if the direction of the annual rings is alternated in consecutive pieces. Thus the warpage of one piece counteracts the warpage of the next.

Lay out the pieces, as shown in Figure 22:1, and make a large pencilled

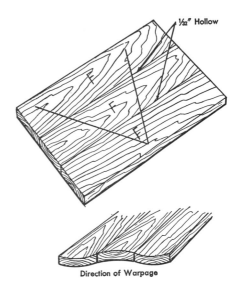

Fig. 22:1   Edge-to-edge Glue Joint

"V" across the pieces so they will be glued together in the correct order. The edges of the pieces must now be planed to fit each other. Each piece should be planed so that the edge is straight and square with the face. If the pieces are long, the joint should be planed so that it will be $\frac{1}{32}$" to $\frac{1}{64}$" open in the centre. This is called a *hollow glue* or *spring joint*. The reason for the slight hollow is that most wood contains an excess of moisture at the time the joint is made. The wood tends to dry out more at the ends, causing it to shrink more there. To compensate for this, the centre is left slightly hollow so that when the shrinkage takes place there will be equal pressure along the full length of the joint. This tends to prevent the joints from opening up at the ends. This hollow is invisible when the work has been glued and clamped. A hollow need not be left in short stock.

When the edges have all been fitted, place the work in two or more bar clamps. Check the joints before applying the glue. When the pressure is applied, the joints should be almost invisible.

Dowel joint

The dowel joint was probably the first type of wood joint used by man, as wooden pegs (dowels) were the first method of fastening two pieces together. Dowels are still used extensively, although not quite in the same form. Many fine pieces of well-preserved furniture that were made many centuries ago and are now found in our museums are held together entirely with wooden pegs or dowels, with no glue, nails, or screws. This furniture is still serviceable today and in excellent condition.

Dowel joints are relatively easy to construct. They may be used in conjunction with such joints as the edge-to-edge joint just described or mitre or

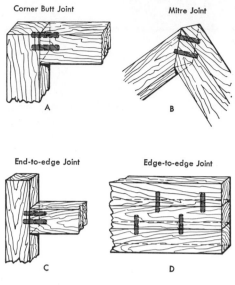

Fig. 22:2   Dowel Joints

butt joints, shown in Figure 22:2, to give extra strength.

The dowels are generally made in long lengths from a hard wood such as maple or birch. They are made in diameters from $\frac{1}{4}$" to $\frac{3}{4}$". The size depends on the thickness of the wood to be joined, the $\frac{3}{8}$" being the most common size used. A general rule for the length of the dowel is that it should be approximately seven times the diameter. The diameter of the dowel should be approximately $\frac{1}{3}$ the thickness of the wood being joined.

A groove $\frac{1}{8}$" deep should be cut the full length of the dowel to allow the excess air and glue to be forced out of the bottom of the hole. A more effective means of distributing the glue is to cut a spiral groove in the dowel, as shown in Figure 22:3. The dowels should have

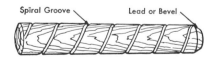

Fig. 22:3   Dowel

a slight lead or bevel on the end so that the glue will not be scraped off the side of the hole as it enters.

Dowels are seldom used singly; two should be used to prevent any pivot action that might take place. If the joint is wide, three should be used.

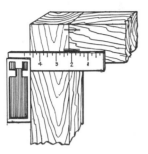

Fig. 22:4 Locating the Dowels on the Face of the Work

How to lay out a dowel joint

1. If an end of one piece is to be butted to the edge of another, the location of the dowels should be marked on the face of the work, as shown in Figure 22:4.

2. Place the two surfaces to be butted together side by side and in a upright position in the vise, as shown in Figures 22:5 and 22:6.

3. Square lines across both pieces at the correct locations using a sharp pencil or knife (see Figure 22:5).

4. Set the marking gauge to exactly half the thickness of the stock and scribe a line from the face side of the work.

5. Make a punch mark where these two lines intersect. This will be the exact centre for the dowel location.

Fig. 22:5 Laying Out a Dowel Joint

Fig. 22:6 Laying Out an End-to-edge Dowel Joint

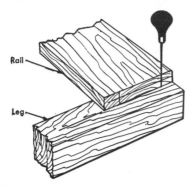

Fig. 22:7 Rail-to-leg Dowel Joint

If one of the pieces is thicker than the other, as is the case when attaching a rail to a table leg, the dowel centres can be located as shown in Figure 22:7.

If dowels are to be used in an edge-to-edge joint, they can be laid out as shown in Figure 22:8.

Select the correct-size auger bit for the dowels being used. When starting to bore, make sure the point of the bit is in the hole made by the scratch awl at the intersection of the lines. Keep the bit perpendicular to the surface of the wood. If the holes are not straight, or are not started correctly, the two pieces will not be properly aligned (see Figure 22:9).

A better job can be made by using a dowelling jig, which, if properly set on the work, ensures that the holes will be correctly located and bored at a right angle to the face of the work. Figure 22:10 illustrates one of these dowelling jigs.

A fast and accurate method of locating the centre for dowel holes is by using metal dowel centres. These are flanged cylindrical metal plugs (made in sizes ranging from ¼" to ¾", with ⅜" the most popular) which fit into the bored hole leaving a sharp point projecting. Thus, when the holes in one piece are laid out and bored, and when the dowel centres are inserted and the mating parts pressed together, the dowel centre points will accurately

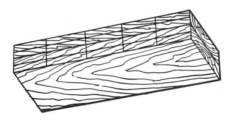

Fig. 22:8 Dowel Location for Edge-to-edge Joint

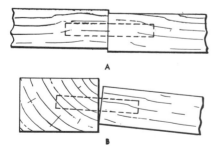

Fig. 22:9 The Result of Poor Alignment of Dowels

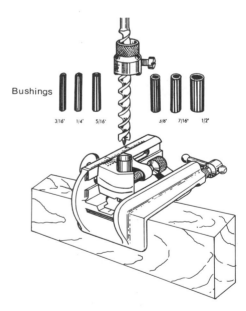

Bushings

3/16" 1/4" 5/16"   3/8" 7/16" 1/2"

Stanley Tools

Fig. 22:10 Dowelling Jig

locate the centres for the holes in the second piece. Dowel centres are shown in Figure 22:11.

Assembling a dowel joint

The dowels should be cut slightly shorter than the combined depth of the two holes. Insert the dowels and fit the two members together dry, before final gluing.

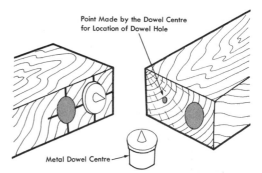

Fig. 22:11 Locating Dowel Holes Using Dowel Centres

Mortise-and-tenon joint

The mortise-and-tenon joint may be considered one of the stronger although more difficult joints to make. There are many variations of this useful joint, but we will only describe the *blind mortise-and-tenon joint*, because it is the one most often used. This joint is shown in Figure 22:12.

The mortise-and-tenon joint is used extensively for furniture, window sashes, and doors.

The *tenon* is the projecting part of one section of the joint, and the *mortise* the corresponding recess into which the tenon fits. The thickness of the tenon should be approximately ⅓ of the total thickness of the stock. The type of mortise-and-tenon joint and the length of the tenon will depend on the width of the stock.

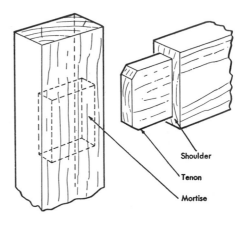

Fig. 22:12 Blind Mortise-and-tenon Joint

To lay out the tenon

1. From the end of the stock, measure the length of the tenon, and square a line all the way round the piece (see line A in Figure 22:13). This is called the *shoulder* of the tenon.

2. On the shoulder of the tenon lay out the thickness of the tenon (points B in Figure 22:13). From these two points, scribe lines on the two edges and the end of the piece as shown. A marking gauge can be used for this. However, it is faster and more accurate to use a mortise gauge that

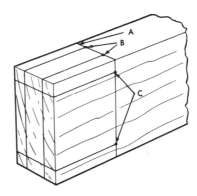

Fig. 22:13 Layout of a Tenon

157

has two scriber points, so that both sides of the tenon can be laid out at one time. Such a gauge is shown in Figure 3:25. Always scribe from the face side of the work.

3. Locate points C of Figure 22:13, which represent the width of the tenon, and scribe lines from these points on the sides and end of the piece in the same manner as for the thickness of the tenon.

To cut the tenon

1. With the work upright in the vise and using the back saw, cut along the lines representing the width and the thickness of the tenon, remembering to cut on the waste side of the lines (see Figure 22:14).

2. With the work on its side in the vise or on a bench hook, make the shoulder cuts (line A, Figure 22:13) until the waste stock falls free. Care should be taken not to cut into the tenon and so weaken it.

To lay out the mortise

1. With a try square, lay out lines A and B, as in Figure 22:15. These lines

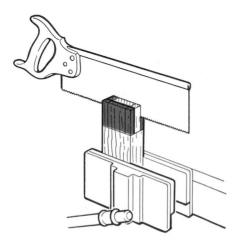

Fig. 22:14 Cutting a Tenon

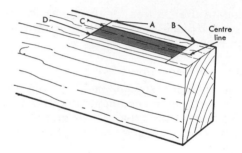

Fig. 22:15 Layout of a Mortise

represent the length of the mortise, which should be slightly larger than the width of the tenon.

2. With the mortise gauge, lay out lines C and D. Set the mortise gauge to the same width as you did for marking the thickness on the tenon.

3. Lay out a centre line midway between these two lines.

To cut the mortise

1. Fasten the stock firmly in the vise with the scribed edge up.

2. With a brace and bit the same diameter as the width of the mortise, bore a hole at either end of the mortise layout. The point of the bit must be started on the centre line. Keep the bit in a perfectly perpendicular position when boring. A depth gauge should be used so that the mortise will be cut slightly deeper than the length of the tenon.

3. Bore as many holes as are required between the two end holes. Each hole should slightly overlap the next (see Figure 22:16).

4. When all the holes have been bored, cut out the remaining material, using a mortise chisel and a mallet.

The mortise may be cut by using only a mortise chisel and a mallet without first using the brace and bit. This method works very well with soft wood. A mortise chisel the same width as the

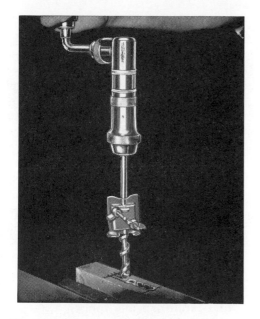

Fig. 22:16 Boring the Holes for a Mortise

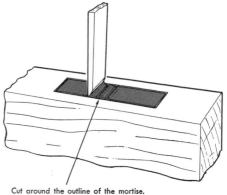

Cut around the outline of the mortise.
Then start from the centre and work towards the ends.

Fig. 22:18 Cutting a Mortise with a Mortise Chisel

mortise-and-tenon, the *stub mortise-and-tenon*, the *open mortise-and-tenon*, the *double mortise-and-tenon*, and the *mortise-and-tenon with a key*. These joints are shown in Figures 22:19 to 22:24.

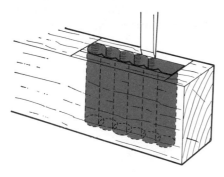

Fig. 22:17 Cutting Out Remaining Material with a Mortise Chisel

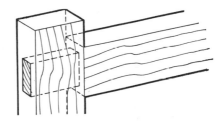

Fig. 22:19 Through Mortise-and-tenon Joint

thickness of the tenon should be used. Do not attempt to remove too much stock with the chisel at one time (see Figure 22:18).

Some final fitting may be necessary to make the joint fit snugly. Smear glue liberally on the tenon before clamping.

Other types of mortise-and-tenon joints are the *through mortise-and-tenon*, where the tenon goes all the way through the piece, the *haunch*

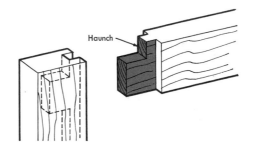

Haunch

Fig. 22:20 Haunch Mortise-and-tenon Joint

159

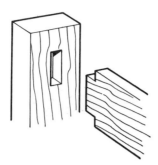

Fig. 22:21 Stub Mortise-and-tenon Joint

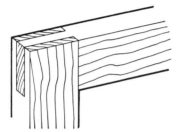

Fig. 22:22 Open Mortise-and-tenon Joint

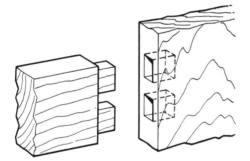

Fig. 22:23 Double Mortise-and-tenon Joint Used in Door Construction

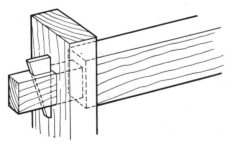

Fig. 22:24 Mortise and Tenon with a Key Used Where Joint Must Be Taken Apart

Cross-lap joint

The cross-lap joint is often called the *half-lap joint* because an equal amount of material is removed from each piece, making the surfaces of the two pieces flush or even. There are several variations of this joint. Four of these are shown in Figures 22:25 to 22:28.

How to lay out a centre cross-lap joint

1. Set one piece over the other at the position of the joint, as shown in Figure 22:29, and mark the cross-lines at both edges of the pieces as shown.

2. Square the lines across the surface of both pieces, using a try square and a knife or a sharp pencil.

3. Scribe a line for the depth of the notch with a marking gauge. This depth should be one-half the thickness of the pieces.

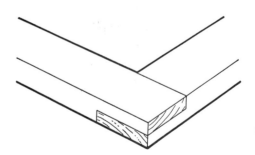

Fig. 22:25 Corner Lap Joint

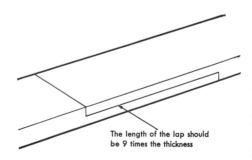

The length of the lap should be 9 times the thickness

Fig. 22:26 End Lap Joint

4. Extend the lines from the surface of the pieces on both edges down to the depth mark just made.

How to cut a lap joint

1. With a back saw, make a cut to the correct depth just inside the cross-lines on both pieces.

2. Make several cuts between the lines down to the same depth, as shown in Figure 22:30.

3. With a socket chisel and mallet, remove the waste stock, chiselling from both sides of the piece to prevent the wood from splitting out below the depth mark (see Figure 22:31).

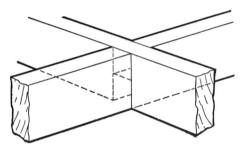

Fig. 22:27 Centre Lap Joint

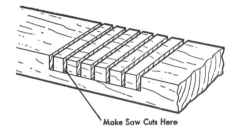

Fig. 22:30

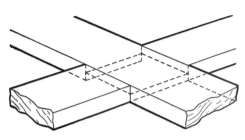

Fig. 22:28 Edge Lap Joint

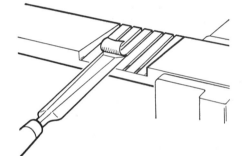

Fig. 22:31 Removing Waste Stock with a Chisel

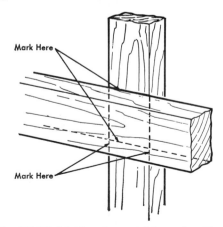

Fig. 22:29 Making Layout Lines for Cross Lap Joint

Fig. 22:32 All Wood Removed

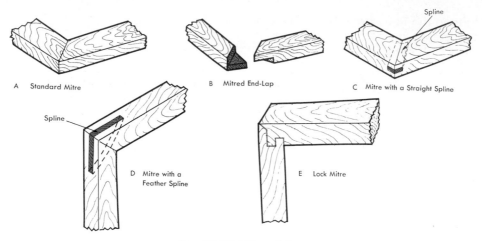

A Standard Mitre

B Mitred End-Lap

Spline

C Mitre with a Straight Spline

Spline

D Mitre with a
Feather Spline

E Lock Mitre

Fig. 22:33 Mitre Joints

4. Fit the two pieces together for a trial assembly. Some fitting may be necessary. The pieces should fit snugly, but it should not be necessary to drive them together.

Mitre joint

The mitre joint is essentially a butt joint that has been cut to 45° so that when the two pieces are placed together they will form a right angle, or a 90° corner, with no end grain exposed. Mitre cuts may be made at other angles, such as 30° to make a six-sided figure. However, the 45° mitre is the one most frequently cut because it is required for making all manner of small frames. Several types of mitre joints are shown in Figure 22:33.

The best method of cutting a mitre joint is to use a *mitre box*, which may be either the hand-made type illustrated in Figure 22:34, or the metal mitre box, which requires a special back saw, shown in Figure 22:35. A more accurate cut can be made with the metal mitre box, and it may be set to cut any desired angle. It is equipped with an adjustable stop that can be set

when you wish to cut duplicate pieces of exactly the same length.

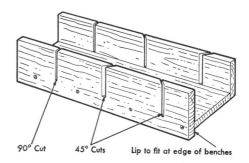

90° Cut   45° Cuts   Lip to fit at edge of benches

Fig. 22:34 Wooden Mitre Box

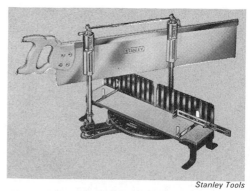

Stanley Tools

Fig. 22:35 Metal Mitre Box and Saw

162

In laying out and cutting a mitre it is important that the piece be measured accurately to length and that the saw cut be made on the waste side of the line. The mitre box will determine the correct angle if the work is held securely against the back of the box.

Mitre joints are generally held with glue and nails, although dowels are sometimes used for extra strength.

Dado joint

A *dado* is a groove cut across the grain of the wood. When another piece is fitted into this groove it is called a *dado joint* (see Figure 22:36). The dado joint is a strong, neat method of joining the end of one piece to the side of another. You probably have often seen cupboards or bookcases where grooves have been cut in the upright end section and the shelves set into them. This is a good example of a dado joint. Dado joints are also used in stepladders. In general the depth of a dado should be 1/3 the thickness of the stock.

To lay out and cut a dado joint

Square the end of one piece. Place this piece in the desired position and mark on either side with a knife or a sharp pencil for the dado joint, as shown in Figure 22:37. Extend the lines down both edges of the piece. With the marking gauge, mark the depth of the dado. Using a back saw, cut just inside the two lines to the correct depth.

Remove the wood between the lines with a mallet and a socket chisel. Fit the two pieces together for a trial assembly. Some final fitting may be necessary to make the joint fit snugly. The pieces should not have to be driven together.

If the dado is too snug, do not attempt to widen it by chiselling or filing. The use of sandpaper or a finely adjusted block plane on the insert will ensure a

neater fit. Where it is not desirable to have the dado exposed on the face edge of the work a *stopped dado joint* is used. The dado does not run the full width of the stock (see Figure 22:38).

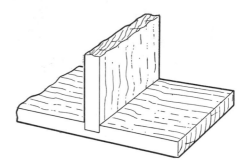

Fig. 22:36 Dado Joint

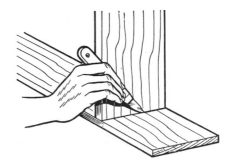

Fig. 22:37 Marking the Layout for a Dado Joint

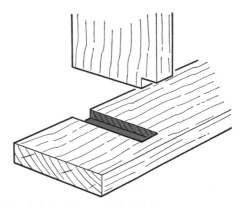

Fig. 22:38 Stopped Dado Joint

163

Fig. 22:39 Making a Dado Cut Using a Router

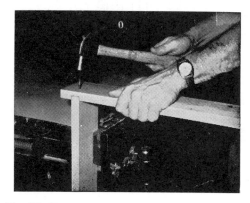

Fig. 22:40 Assembling a Dado Joint

Rabbet joint

The rabbet joint is actually a dado joint that is made at the end of the piece (see Figures 22:41 and 22:42). It is used mainly for corner construction. The front of a drawer is often fastened to the sides in this manner.

A rabbet cut may also be made the full length of a piece.

To lay out and cut a rabbet joint

Square the end of the pieces and place them together in the correct location. As shown in Figure 22:43, mark along the edge of piece number 1 with a knife

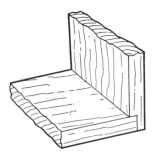

Fig. 22:41 Rabbet Joint

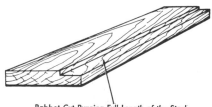

Rabbet Cut Running Full Length of the Stock

Fig. 22:42

164

or a sharp pencil. Continue this line down the edge of the piece. Scribe a line to the correct depth on both edges and on the end of piece number 2. With the back saw, cut just inside the line to the required depth. Remove the waste wood with a socket chisel and mallet. Do any necessary trimming with a sharp chisel to make the pieces fit properly. Both the rabbet and the dado

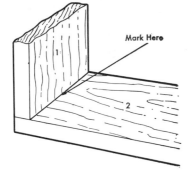

Fig. 22:43 Layout of a Rabbet Joint

Fig. 22:44 Dovetail Half-lap Joint

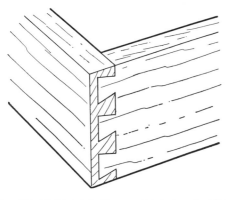

Fig. 22:45 Multiple Dovetail Joint — As Used for Drawer Construction

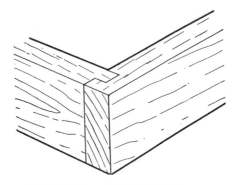

Fig. 22:46 Dado and Rabbet Joint

Fig. 22:47 Dovetail Dado Joint

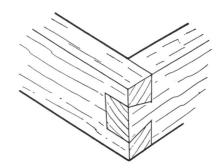

Fig. 22:48 Through Single Dovetail

165

Plain Fact

THE HOLDING POWER OF A WOOD JOINT DEPENDS ON HOW WELL THE PIECES FIT. NO AMOUNT OF GLUE WILL MAKE A POOR-FITTING JOINT SECURE.

joints can be nailed, screwed, or glued together.

There are a great many other joints that are used in woodwork. Some of these are shown in Figures 22:44 to 22:48.

ASSIGNMENT

1. What are the requirements of a good wood joint?

Edge-to-edge joints

2. Why is it more advisable to use two narrow boards glued edge to edge than one wide piece?

3. Make a drawing of three boards ready for gluing. Show all the markings that indicate their correct position.

Dowel joints

4. Why were dowel joints the first type of wood joints used?

5. In what general types of wood joints are dowels used?

6. (a) From what type of wood are dowels generally made?
   (b) In what sizes are dowels made?

(c) What is the common length for individual dowels?

7. Why is a groove cut in the side of a dowel? Why do they have a lead?

8. Explain how end-to-edge dowel joints are laid out. (You may use diagrams for your explanation.)

9. How is a dowelling jig used?

Mortise-and-tenon joints

10. List three types of mortise-and-tenon joints, and three places in which they are used.

11. What should be the thickness of a tenon on a piece of stock 1⅛" thick?

12. What is the difference between a marking gauge and a mortise gauge?

13. Why is a centre line drawn on the mortise layout?

14. Describe how the mortise is cut.

Cross-lap joints

15. Why is a cross-lap joint often referred to as a half-lap joint?

16. Make a sketch of three types of lap joints.

17. Describe how to lay out a centre cross-lap joint.

18. Why should the wood be chiselled from both edges of the piece when making a cross-lap joint?

Mitre joints

19. What is meant by a mitre cut?
20. List the advantages and disadvantages of the metal and the wooden mitre boxes.
21. If you wish to make an eight-sided frame using eight individual pieces, at what angle would you make the cut at each end of them? At each end of the twelve pieces for a twelve-sided figure?
22. How are mitre joints held together?

Dado and rabbet joints

23. What is a dado cut?
24. List four wooden articles in which you might use dado joints.
25. What is the difference between a dado and a rabbet joint?
26. List the steps in making a rabbet joint.
27. How are dado and rabbet joints held together?
28. How would you lay out and cut the joints shown in Figure 22:46?

scraping, sanding, and preparation for finishing

It is impossible to obtain a good finish on work unless it has been properly prepared. There are many types of finish that may be used, but none of them is made to cover poor workmanship. In fact, the finish will magnify the defects. Scratches or other marks that may not be detected or may be only slightly visible on the bare wood will show up as noticeable blemishes on the finished work.

Successful finishing begins with having the work properly sanded and free from dents, scratches, chips, and other imperfections. Some dents can be removed by placing several thicknesses of wet cloth over them and then pressing a hot iron on the cloth, keeping the iron moving so as not to scorch the work. The steam created swells the wood fibres and brings them back to their original position. This process may have to be repeated several times to raise the dent completely. The spot can be sanded when dry. All nails should be set below the surface but should not be filled until one coat of finishing material has been applied. If they are filled first, the oil from the filler soaks into the wood and the filler falls out. However, if a protective coat is first spread on the work to seal the wood fibres, the filler will remain in place.

You should take enough time to do a good job of cleaning and sanding. Having spent hours to make a project, you would be wise to spend a little more time in scraping and sanding so that a worthwhile finish can be obtained.

Scrapers

Scrapers are wood-smoothing tools that make a finer cut than the plane. They are used just prior to sanding to remove plane marks and other defects too

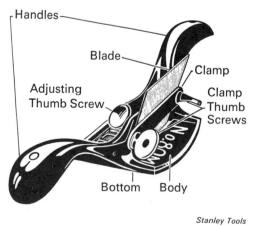

Fig. 23:1   Cabinet Scraper

Handles
Blade
Clamp
Adjusting Thumb Screw
Clamp Thumb Screws
Bottom   Body

Stanley Tools

Fig. 23:2   Hand Scraper

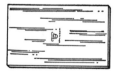
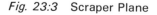

Fig. 23:3   Scraper Plane

small to plane off but too deep to sand out.

There are several types of scrapers, each made for a different purpose. Figures 23:1 to 23:4 illustrate some of these.

The scraper removes a fine shaving by means of a burred cutting edge, while the plane uses a sharp bevelled edge. These different cutting actions are illustrated in Figure 23:5.

Figures 23:6 illustrates the shape of the burr formed on a hand scraper. The procedure for sharpening scrapers is dealt with later in the book.

When using a hand scraper on a large flat surface, push with your two thumbs in the centre and near the cutting edge (as shown in Figure 23:7). This curves the scraper slightly and makes it cut at the centre section. On smaller surfaces the scraper may be

Millers Falls Co.

Fig. 23:4   Hoe Scraper

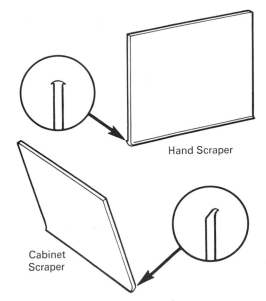

Hand Scraper

Cabinet Scraper

Fig. 23:6   Burrs Formed on Scrapers

Cutting Action of a Plane.

Cutting or Scraping Action of a Scraper.

Fig. 23:5   Cutting Action of Planes and Scrapers

Press Here and Spring to a Slight Curve

Fig. 23:7   Method of Holding a Hand Scraper

169

pushed or pulled, depending on which is the more convenient way to get at the various parts of the work. Since a very fine cut is being made, the scraper can be used to cut with or against the grain. The cabinet scraper and the scraper plane should be used on flat surfaces only.

Sandpaper

It is important that you use the correct method of sanding and select the proper grade of paper for the work you are doing.

The name *sandpaper* is a general term given to all abrasive papers used for smoothing wood. The name originated many years ago when paper was coated with beach sand. Today, in spite of its name, no sand is actually used in its manufacture. Modern sandpaper is made from four finely ground minerals. Two of these are natural rock substances and two are manufactured in electric furnaces.

The two natural minerals

Flint quartz is used for making flint paper. It has an off-white colour and is used in the manufacture of the least expensive, and also the least effective, type of sandpaper. The grit is not as sharp as that in other papers, so that it cuts more slowly and wears out more quickly. It is used extensively for sanding painted surfaces.

Garnet, when ground, makes a very hard, sharp, dark red grit. When made up into sandpaper, it is sold in sheets or roll stock. Garnet paper is used extensively in industry both for hand sanding and on power sanders. It is more expensive than flint paper but is of a much better quality.

The artificial minerals

Aluminum oxide is made in an electric furnace from bauxite, the raw material from which aluminum is made. It is reddish-brown, very hard, and sharp. Aluminum oxide paper may be used on either wood or metal.

Silicon carbide is also made in an electric furnace at very high temperatures from silicon (sand) and coke. This is the way nature makes diamonds from the heat and pressure of the earth. Man, by using the same method, has been able to make grit that is almost as hard as diamond. Silicon carbide paper is gray or black in colour and may be used either dry or with water or mineral spirits. It is often referred to as *wet dry paper*.

Grit type and size

Sandpaper is made (a) with an open grit (the particles are not close together and the paper may be seen through the grit) or (b) with a closed grit (the particles are spread thickly). The closed grit paper cuts faster and lasts longer when used on clean wood. However, for sanding gummy wood or painted surfaces, open paper is superior because it does not clog up as rapidly.

Sandpaper is graded as to coarseness by the size of the grit used. It ranges from a very fine 10/0 to a medium of 2/0. These sizes are stamped on the back of the sheet and are read "two 0", "three 0", "four 0", and so on. The coarse sizes are ½, 1, 1½, 2, 2½, and 3. The more 0's, the finer the paper; the larger the whole number, the coarser the paper. A more recent method of designating the coarseness of sandpaper by number is shown on page 171. The corresponding 0 sizes of garnet paper are indicated.

Whatever the grade of paper, the size of grit will be uniform, as any oversized grit in a fine sheet of paper would cause scratches. The grit is filtered through a silk screen with various-sized openings for the coarse and medium grades. For

170

	Sandpaper Number	The Corresponding O Sizes of Garnet Paper
Very Fine	280	8 / 0
	240	7 / 0
	220	6 / 0
Fine	180	5 / 0
	150	4 / 0
	120	3 / 0
Medium	100	2 / 0
	80	1 / 0
	60	1 / 2
Coarse	50	1
	40	1 ½
Very Coarse	36	2
	30	2 ½
	24	3

Fig. 23:8 Sanding with Tungsten Carbide

the fine grades a flotation system is used whereby the fine grit will drop to the bottom of a liquid. The grit is applied to the adhesive-coated paper by an electrostatic process that stands all the grit particles on end, thus making the paper cut much faster.

Tungsten carbide

A recent development in abrasive material is tungsten carbide, an extremely hard, manufactured carbon material used for tips on steel-cutting tools. The carbide is broken up into fine particles and bonded onto thin steel plates. The metal sheets are made in convenient sizes and used on sanding blocks in the same manner as sandpaper (see Figure 23:8). If the surface does not become clogged with glue or paint or otherwise damaged, the extremely hard cutting surface will last indefinitely. This type of material can be used only on flat surfaces. Only fine and medium grades are available. Wood-cutting files are also made with a tungsten carbide cutting surface.

How to sand

To make the sanding operation more effective and less tedious there are a few techniques that should be followed. To sand a flat surface true, some type of sanding block should be used. Several types of blocks are sold commercially for this purpose, or one can be made. It should have a felt or rubber pad to cushion the paper. An unpadded block should never be used for finish sanding. If a chip or piece of grit gets between the paper and the block, it will make scratches that are very difficult to remove.

Begin the sanding with coarse paper. Sand at an angle to the grain. This will level the work but leave fine scratches over the entire surface. To remove these, follow with a medium grit paper, sanding with the grain. If the wood has a coarse open grain, such as oak, sand at an angle to avoid enlarging the pores and removing the soft part of the grain. Finish the sanding with a fine paper, working with the grain. Pencil any small irregularities that remain, and sand until they disappear. Before the final sanding the work is sometimes given a wash coat of thin shellac. This will stiffen up any loose wood fibres, which can then be easily sanded off.

To produce a true flat surface by hand sanding you must use a uniform stroke of equal pressure for the full length of

171

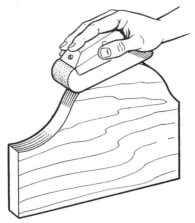

Fig. 23:9   Use a sanding block that will allow the sandpaper to reach all parts of the edge.

the work. Sand with short strokes and move along the work, overlapping each stroke. If square edges are required, hold the paper flat, and do not bend it round the corners or edges.

The individual parts of a project should be sanded before being assembled in order to take care of many of those hard-to-get-at corners and because single parts and sub-assemblies are much more easily sanded when they can be placed flat on a bench. The work should be organized so there will be a minimum of sanding on the completely assembled project. Curved edges can be sanded as shown in Figure 23:9.

ASSIGNMENT

Scrapers

1. What is the main purpose of a scraper?
2. Name four types of scrapers.
3. How does the cutting action of the scraper differ from that of the plane?
4. How should the hand scraper be held for most effective results on large flat surfaces?
5. Why may the scraper be used to cut with or against the grain of the wood?

Sandpapers and sanding

6. Why is it absolutely essential that all scratches and defects be removed from a project before any finishing material is applied?
7. How may a dent be removed from a project without removing any wood?
8. Why should you wait until a coat of finishing material is applied before filling nail holes?
9. Why could we say that sandpaper is now improperly named?
10. Name and describe three types of sandpaper. What abrasive material is used for the manufacture of each?
11. (a) Which is the finer sandpaper: 2/0 or 4/0?
    (b) Give the corresponding number sizes of 2/0 and 4/0 sandpaper.
12. How are the particles of grit divided and attached to the paper backing?
13. How does tungsten carbide abrasive differ from sandpaper?
14. Why should an unpadded sanding block not be used for finish sanding?
15. What three grades of sandpaper should be used in preparing a piece of work for stain or shellac?
16. Why should individual parts be sanded before they are assembled?

CHAPTER TWENTY-FOUR

finishing — part 1

It is the finish applied to a well sanded base that adds beauty and durability to a project. For this reason it is important that the correct type of finish be selected and properly applied.

There are three general classifications of wood finishes: stain, natural, and paint or enamel. There are, of course, many variations of each of these types and others are being developed all the time. The type of finish used on a project depends on several factors, such as:

(a) The type of wood used. Some woods, such as walnut, oak, and mahogany, are better adapted to natural finishes. These woods have an attractive grain formation as well as a distinctive colour. Other woods, such as maple, birch, and beech, have an attractive grain formation but are generally considered too light in colour for natural finishes and because of this they are often stained. Still other woods, such as basswood and pine, are generally considered better adapted to a paint finish.

(b) The use to which the furniture is to be put. Kitchen furniture and outdoor furniture are generally painted, while other furniture more often has a stained or natural finish.

(c) The type of finish on the other furniture that the new project must match.

Stained finishes

We shall consider first the stained finish. Wood is stained to give it a desired colour, to bring out the natural beauty of the grain, and, in some cases, to provide some measure of protection for the wood. Stains are made in the colours of dark-coloured woods such as walnut, oak, or mahogany, either to make light-coloured woods resemble the more highly coloured woods, or to deepen the colour of the dark woods. Most stains can be classified as: water stain, oil stain, or spirit or lacquer stain. These stains differ mainly in the solvent that is used to dissolve the colour pigments.

Water stains

These are made by mixing colouring materials that are soluble in hot water. They are brilliant, have an even penetration, and are non-fading. Water stains, however, have the disadvantage of causing the grain to rise, a factor that makes resanding the work necessary.

Oil stains

There are two general types of oil stains —*penetrating oil stains* and *pigment oil stains*. Oil stains are not as bright, nor do they penetrate as deeply, as water stains, but they have the advantage of not raising the grain of the wood. Penetrating oil stains are made with aniline and coal tar dyes using light oils such as turpentine, naphtha, or benzol as a solvent or base. They are mixed when hot. Pigment oil stains are made from colour pigments similar to those used for tinting paint. These are mixed with linseed oil. Oil stains are very convenient to apply because they do not dry too rapidly and can be brushed over several times if necessary so that no lap joints will show. They are referred to as *wiping stains* because they can be wiped over while they are still wet to make the stain lighter and the grain show through.

Oil stains, if not protected by shellac or varnish, tend to fade when exposed to the light. The stain will bleed (dissolve slightly) if varnish is applied directly over it. This can be avoided by giving the work a wash coat of shellac over the stain before varnishing. Oil stains are more expensive than water stains but are used more extensively because of their convenience and their easy application.

Spirit stains
These stains have a base of alcohol to which pigments or dyes are added. They are bright, have good penetration, but will fade if not protected by varnish. Shellac should not be used directly over spirit stains as the alcohol in the shellac will dissolve the stain. The main advantage of these stains is that they are quick-drying. They can be recoated in ten to fifteen minutes. This factor makes them very popular in industry because the work can be stained, filled, and varnished all in the same day. They are referred to in industry as *N.G.R.* (non-grain-raising) stains. Their disadvantage is that they are difficult to apply with a brush because they dry so rapidly; a spray gun is generally used.

How to apply stain

The following points should be observed when applying oil stain:

1. The work must be free from all dust.

2. As end grain has more suction and absorbs stain more readily than flat grain, it should be given a coat of the oil that has been used as the solvent or base of the stain. With most oil stains linseed oil can be used for this purpose. The oil should be allowed to dry before staining.

3. Apply the stain with a brush or cloth. Start on the unexposed portion of the project. Work stain into all the angles or awkward spots, making sure no spots are missed.

4. Allow the stain to penetrate for a few minutes or until it becomes dull. Then wipe it over with a soft cloth to remove the excess stain and to make a more uniform colour. Do not wipe too soon, or too much of the stain will be removed; but do not wait too long, or the wiping will make the job streaky. In general, the longer the stain is left before wiping, the darker the finish will be.

5. Let the work dry for twenty-four hours in a dust-free area before recoating.

The same procedure is followed when applying water stain except that a sponge coat of clear water is applied first. This raises the grain. After it dries, it is sanded down before staining. This minimizes the amount of sanding required after staining.

Spirit stains are seldom brushed on because they dry so quickly. A spray gun should be used. Spirit stains are not wiped and therefore must be applied evenly so that no laps or streaks will appear. Dark patches may be lightened by rubbing with a cloth that has been moistened with spirits.

Wood fillers

There are two types of wood fillers — *paste filler* and *liquid filler*. Either is used as a base for a shellac or varnish finish. We do not refer here to the thick commercial wood fillers that are used to cover defects, nail-holes, open joints, or other signs of poor workmanship. A careful workman has no need for this type of filler.

Paste or liquid fillers are required on

Fig. 24:1 Wiping an Oil Stain

most woods to fill the open pores of the wood and make a smooth surface. If the pores are not filled, the finish will be uneven and pitted.

Woods are divided into two general classes — open-grain woods and closed-grain woods. The open-grain woods, such as oak, ash, or elm, have a very coarse grain with large pores that require a paste filler, while the closed-grain woods, such as birch, cherry, or maple, which have a finer wood texture, require only a liquid filler. Some of the soft woods, such as pine, basswood, or cedar, which have a very close grain, do not require a filler of any type; however, a liquid sealer of some type should be used. No two species of woods have identical wood textures. With different-sized wood cells it is difficult to classify all woods as having definite closed or open grains; some are in between. The filler used must be mixed according to the wood.

Paste wood fillers may be bought already prepared from the paint store, or they can be mixed. The ingredients of fillers vary somewhat according to the wood on which they are used, but a more or less standard mixture that is used by many finishers can be made as follows:

1 pint boiled linseed oil
2 pints turpentine
1/3 pint Japan drier

To this mixture add enough silex powder to make a thick paste. Stir the mixture well and strain through a wire screen. Thin with benzine or naphtha to the consistency of thick cream.

The basic ingredient of filler is the silica powder, which fills the wood pores. It is made from very finely ground quartz rock, is pure white in colour, and is commonly called *silex*. Although other powders, such as cornstarch, are sometimes used in fillers, silex is considered the best for general use. Stain may be added to the filler either to darken the stain already on the work, or to stain and fill the work in one operation. This is sometimes done to save time but is not as good a method as the two-coat application.

Liquid filler may also be bought already prepared or it may be mixed. The

175

ingredients for this filler, as used by many finishers, are:

1 gallon rubbing alcohol
1 quart turpentine
1 pint Japan drier
2½ lb. silex powder

Stir well and thin with benzine or turpentine to an easy brushing consistency. If the filler is to serve the dual purpose of a stain and filler, colour must be added.

How to apply wood filler

Paste wood filler should be applied to open-grain woods after the work has been stained in order to allow the stain to penetrate into the wood but still leave open the pores that must be filled.

The filler should be applied liberally and worked well into the wood fibres with a stiff brush or cloth. Brush across the grain, working the filler well into the pores of the wood. The excess filler must be rubbed off with excelsior, burlap, or fine shavings. Before being rubbed, the filler should be allowed to set five to ten minutes or until it loses its wet, shiny appearance. Rub vigorously across the grain. No surplus filler should remain, or it will create a foggy appearance when succeeding coats are applied. Care should be taken not to rub too hard with the grain, or the filler may be drawn out of the wood pores. Let the work dry for twenty-four hours before recoating.

Liquid fillers should be applied in the same manner as paste fillers, but less wiping is required.

In some cases the stain is sealed by giving it a wash coat consisting of 1 part shellac to 4 parts alcohol before the filler is applied. The advantage of sealing the stain is to prevent the filler from softening the stain and to make the filler easier to wipe. The filler, in turn, is generally sealed with the same mixture before finish coats of shellac, varnish, or lacquer are used. On many soft woods, such as fir or pine, the bare wood is sealed instead of using a filler of any type. The pores are sealed instead of being filled. The sealer used may be either a diluted shellac or one of the many commercial sealers that are sold for this purpose. Some of these lacquer sealers are now used extensively on hardwood floors in place of fillers.

Shellac

Pure shellac is manufactured from a gum called *lac*, which is deposited on the branches of certain species of tropical trees by swarms of tiny lac insects. The gum-laden twigs and branches, which are called *lac sticks*, are gathered by workers and the dark, resinous, gummy material is heated and separated from the bark and wood, and then allowed to dry into hard, flake shellac.

The shellac gum can be dissolved in denatured alcohol to a liquid state so that it can be brushed or sprayed. The amount of alcohol used to dissolve the shellac gum determines the grade or strength of the shellac. Most good shellacs are a four-pound cut; that is, four pounds of shellac gum are dissolved in one gallon of alcohol. Other grades range from a two-pound to a five-pound cut.

Shellac in its natural form is a dark orange colour, hence the name *orange shellac* when it is used in its natural colour. Orange shellac should be used only on dark-coloured woods. The natural shellac gum must bleached to make *white shellac*, which is used as an almost transparent finish suitable for light-coloured woods. A type of synthetic shellac with a plastic base is now being manufactured.

Shellac may be used as a filler, a sealer, and a base for a wax or varnish finish, or it may be used as a final finish. In some cases it may be used for special finishes, such as French polish or dip-and-rub finish. Shellac makes a hard, bright, smooth finish that dries fairly rapidly. It has, however, the disadvantage that it cannot withstand moisture. The finish will take on a milky look if it comes into contact with moisture. It will not withstand high temperatures either. A shellacked table-top may become gummy if placed in front of a window on a bright sunny day. For these reasons shellac finishes are not as popular as they once were. They have to some extent been replaced by synthetic varnishes; however, shellac is still used and is considered important enough to be discussed here.

How to apply shellac

Shellac may be applied with a spray gun or with a brush. For the first two coats the shellac should be diluted to a two-pound cut; for remaining coats, use a four-pound cut.

When applying shellac, use a soft varnish brush. Use long, running strokes, brushing with the grain of the wood. Work quickly and do not brush back and forth over the work too often, or the shellac will build up in ridges and will show lap marks. If a spot is missed, leave it to be covered in the next coat, as it is very difficult to touch up shellac.

For the first coat allow three to six hours' drying time; for succeeding coats allow twelve hours. Rub the work down between coats with fine sandpaper or steel wool, rubbing with the grain. After each sanding, dust the work with a cloth before recoating. If the cloth is dampened with benzine, it does a better job of picking up all the dust particles.

French polish

This type of finish has been used on fine furniture for many generations. It takes considerable time and care, but the resulting fine finish is worth the effort.

Care must be taken in preparing the surface to have it absolutely free from defects. If the work is to be stained, a water stain must be used. When it is thoroughly dry, apply thin shellac diluted with alcohol to a one-pound cut, which is almost as thin as water. Apply this mixture with a soft cloth rolled into a pad; dip the cloth into the mixture and rub into the work in straight strokes with the grain. When the surface is dry, sand lightly and repeat the operation. After several coats a light sheen will appear. At this stage add a few drops of boiled linseed oil and continue the rubbing, but change to a rotary motion. For each succeeding coat add a little more oil. Continue until the work has a deep, glowing finish.

French polish may also be used to refinish a surface that has become scratched or blemished. For this operation care must be taken to rub in an even circular motion. The secret is to keep the pad in constant motion. Even a slight pause will cause the tacky cloth to stick and leave a rough blemish in the polished surface. If this occurs, the new finish must be removed with alcohol and the French polishing operation started over. Rub with an even circular motion, which produces a series of overlapping circles, until all the surface has been covered. Repeat the operation, refilling the pad with the polishing material as required. During this process the old finish is softened and blends in with the new polish, filling in all scratches and blemishes and producing a hard smooth surface that should last for years.

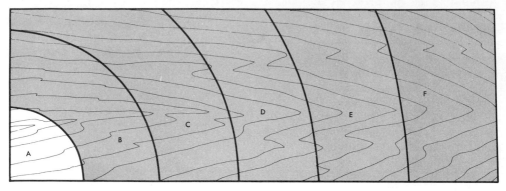

A Well sanded surface

B Stain

C Sealer—protects the colour of the stain and keeps it from bleeding through into the finished coat.

D Paste wood filler—on open-grained woods only.

E Sealer—a diluted coat of same material as the final finish.

F Final shellac, varnish or lacquer finish—one to six coats depending on the finish required.

Note: If the paste filler is omitted, only one coat is required.

Fig. 24:2   Steps in Finishing a Piece of Furniture

Dip-and-rub finish

This finish is similar to the French polish but is a little easier to apply. Over the stain, brush on a thin coat of shellac, and sand smooth.

Make a pad of a clean, soft rag and dip it alternately into containers of white shellac (4-pound cut) and then into pure turpentine. Rub this into the work in a rotary motion, covering the entire surface. Apply four or five coats in the same manner, sanding between coats. This generally produces a rich gloss, but if a brighter polish is desired, allow the work to dry for eighteen hours, and rub with a cloth dipped in boiled linseed oil.

ASSIGNMENT

1. What are the three general types of wood finishes?

2. What factors determine the type of finish that should be used on a project?

Stains

3. Why are wood stains used?

4. List two advantages and one disadvantage of the three types of wood stains.

5. How should end grain be treated to prevent it from absorbing too much stain?

6. Explain the wiping operation that is used when applying oil stain.

7. Why should the work be given a wash coat of water before applying water stain?

8. What precautions must be taken when applying spirit stains?

9. Would you be more likely to use oak stain on a project made of birch or of oak?

10. Define the words *solvent*, *pigments*, and *soluble*.

Fillers

11. Why are paste wood fillers used on open-grain woods?

12. List three open-grain woods and three closed-grain woods.

13. What are the ingredients of liquid wood filler?

14. How is paste wood filler applied?

Shellac

15. What is the base material used for natural shellac?

16. List the advantages and the disadvantages of a shellac finish.

17. List in point form the steps in applying a French polish finish.

finishing — part 2

Varnish

Varnish is a general term that has commonly been used to describe any hard, transparent finish used over stain or as a natural finish to protect and beautify work. It is difficult to list the ingredients of varnish because there are so many types. However, varnishes can be divided into three main classes: oil varnishes, spirit varnishes, and Japan varnishes.

Oil varnishes are made from vegetable oils, such as linseed oil or tung oil, mixed with fossil resin gums, such as congo gum and kauri gum. Fossil resins are hardened or "fossilized" materials from trees that have fallen, been covered over with earth, and become stone-like. They are found in East Africa, the Congo, and New Zealand. They must be heated to mix with the oils. Turpentine and driers are also mixed with oil varnishes.

Spirit varnishes are made with turpentine or shellac and resin gums but have no drying oils. Spirit varnishes dry by evaporation while oil varnishes harden by oxidation. Shellac is the best-known spirit varnish.

Japan varnishes, commonly called *Japan driers*, are drying agents. They are not used as finishing coats but are added to other types of varnish to make them dry faster.

There are many special types and variations of these varnishes, each made for a special purpose. A few of these are listed here:

Spar varnish is used for exterior work. It contains more oil than other varnishes so that it will withstand moisture and temperature extremes.

Floor varnish and *rubbing varnishes* have less oil and more gum to make them especially hard to withstand wear. They are generally quick-drying.

Flat varnish dries with a dull lustre.

Dammar varnish is more transparent than other varnishes.

Varnish stains are varnishes that have been tinted with stains to colour the work as well as to provide a finishing coat.

Spraying varnishes have been thinned so that they can be better used with a spray gun.

Many new types of quick-drying varnish are being made with synthetic resins mixed with light oil, spirits, and a drying agent. These varnishes, which dry in one to four hours, save much time and cut down on the amount of dust that may settle on the wet varnish.

Lacquer

Lacquer is a quick-drying, hard, transparent type of finishing material that could be classified as a varnish. However, it differs in its composition from oil varnish because both the gums and the solvents are synthetic, or manufactured, rather than being natural materials.

Most lacquers have a cellulose base. Cellulose is the chemical name given to any vegetable fibre. Cotton or wood fibres are used for most cellulose materials. Lacquer is made by dissolving cotton that has been treated with nitric acid (nitrated cotton) in a solvent. The solvent used may be ethyl alcohol, acetone, methyl alcohol, or a combination of these materials. Coloured lacquers are made by adding colour pigments. Lacquer dries very rapidly by evaporation, making it difficult to apply with a brush to a large surface. Better results have been obtained by using a spray gun. However, the manufacturers are constantly improving their brushing lacquers and several are now on the market that can be applied successfully with a brush. Brush lacquer is now being extensively used as a sealer and a finishing coat for hardwood floors, while spraying lacquer is used on much of the furniture now being made.

Some of the advantages of lacquers over some varnish finishes are that (a) they do not check or crack as readily; (b) they are not affected by extreme temperatures; (c) they are more moisture-resistant than most varnishes; (d) they dry more rapidly, a factor that makes them so popular in industry; (e) they dry with a deep lustre; (f) grease and dirt can easily be removed by wiping the surface with a dry cloth without injuring the finish.

Some of the disadvantages of lacquers are that (a) they are difficult to apply to a large surface with a brush; (b) they cannot be applied over any other finishing material that contains linseed oil, such as varnish, paint, stain, or enamel; (The lacquer solvent acts as a varnish or paint remover. However, this difficulty can be avoided by applying a coat of thin shellac between the old finish and the lacquer. Those lacquers that have an alcohol solvent can be safely used over oil finishes.) (c) they sometimes shrink in drying, which makes it difficult to build up a smooth surface, especially on porous woods.

Polyester finishes

Closely allied to lacquers are the more recently developed polyester finishes. These are the types of finish that are used on the plastic-covered boards such as Arborite and other commercial counter-top materials. Polyester finishes have been extensively used for some time in industry, but only recently has a type been developed that will harden at room temperature and can be sprayed or brushed on a wood surface.

The derivation of the name *polyester* partially describes this material. *Poly* means "many" or "a very large number", and *ester* is the chemical term for an organic compound that is made by mixing alcohol with an organic acid. Most of these esters are made from petroleum products.

The prepared liquid polyester finishes used for wood are synthetic resin finishes that consist of an ester and another reactive monomer (a material made up of single, unattached molecules). When a small quantity of a third material, a catalyst, is added, the mixture will *polymerize*. That is, the molecules will join together into one unit, which in this case forms a plastic film. It is very important that exactly the correct amount of catalyst is added so that the desired reaction will take place. Manufacturers' directions must be followed closely and only the amount required at one time should be mixed.

The work should be placed with the surface to be finished in a horizontal position because polyester finishes are spread more thickly than other finishes and are self-levelling only if applied to a horizontal surface. On parts that cannot be placed horizontally several thin coats must be applied. The finish may be applied by spraying or by brushing, or sometimes may be allowed to flow on and be levelled with a cardboard scraper. Polyester finishes may be used over old finishes if they are clean and free from major defects. However, they are more often used on new surfaces. In most cases a two-coat application will produce an excellent finish if sanded between coats.

This plastic coating has the advantage of drying to an extremely hard surface with a high lustre that is not affected by temperature changes, water, alcohol, or acid. It also has the advantage of not fading, is resilient, and is resistant to impact and abrasion. It sets quickly, taking only half an hour to harden.

The main disadvantage of a polyester finish is that it must be used as a two-component finish. It is sold by the quart or gallon, with a small separate container of the catalyst to be added in direct proportion to the amount of finish required at one time.

Two synthetic finishing materials that are in popular use and do not require the mixing of two materials before application are (a) *polyurethane*, which is clear and highly resistant to moisture and chemicals, and dries fast with a hard, clear surface, and (b) *epoxy*, a resin material, clear or coloured, which can be applied to wood, fibreglass, metal, or almost any type of surface. Because epoxy is highly resistant to moisture, chemicals, and abrasion it is extensively used on all types of boats.

A great future is predicted for the synthetic-resin-type materials for wood finishing. Through further experimentation still better types of this material are being developed. This is just another recent development of chemical technology that has added to the beauty, value, and efficiency of wood products.

How to apply varnish

Good-quality varnish, if properly applied, provides an air-tight, transparent, durable, and attractive finish. It is not difficult to apply. However, to produce good results these precautions and directions must be followed:

1. The work must be properly clean and smooth.

2. Good-quality varnish and clean brushes must be used.

3. As far as possible the varnishing should be done in a dust-free area.

4. The temperature of the room and the finishing material should be between 70° and 80°.

5. There should be a circulation of clean, warm air, but no cold draughts.

6. If the varnish is cold, place the can in hot water for a few minutes.

7. Begin brushing in the centre of a section and work toward the edges.

8. Brush with the grain with uniform strokes.

9. Do not allow the varnish to "pile up" in corners or to accumulate on the edges. Light strokes with a well-wiped brush will even out the varnish.

10. Follow the manufacturers' directions as to the length of drying time between coats.

Rubbing down a finish

To make a varnished surface perfectly smooth you must rub it with a fine abrasive. The rubbing will remove some of the high shine but will add lustre and depth, the mark of a good-quality hand-rubbed finish. Do not be satisfied with the rough but shiny finish that appears on a freshly varnished or shellacked surface.

The work should be rubbed lightly with dry 3/0 sandpaper or steel wool between the first and second coats. However, finer abrasive materials must be used over succeeding coats so as not to scratch the surface. *Pumice stone* is often used for this rubbing. Pumice is a very finely ground rock. It comes in several grades of coarseness, with the fine and the extra fine being the most commonly used. Pumice stone should never be used dry but should be rubbed on the surface with either water or oil.

There are several methods of rubbing with pumice stone. Some finishers mix the pumice with water to form a paste and rub the work with a cloth or felt pad. (A chalk eraser makes a good pad.) Place some of the paste on the pad and rub in long strokes with the grain. Since pumice stone is fine and does not cut rapidly, it takes considerable rubbing to bring the finish up to the required lustre. Another method sometimes used when rubbing with pumice is to dampen the surface of the work with water and also to dampen the pad before sprinkling the dry pumice on it. Rub in the same manner as with the paste pumice stone.

If a shellac finish is being rubbed, linseed or rubbing oil should be used with the pumice stone in place of water, as moisture will turn shellac a milky colour. Oil can also be used with the pumice stone for a varnish finish, but only over the last coat, because even a slight film of oil between coats of varnish is detrimental to the finish. Pumice stone makes a finer finish with oil than with water.

For a finer finish still, *rottenstone*, a much finer powder, can be used with oil. Rottenstone does not cut but will polish the surface to a satin finish.

In recent years, waterproof, fine *silicon sandpapers* have replaced pumice and rottenstone as materials for rubbing varnish finishes. The 600-grade silicon carbide paper can be used in much the same way as pumice stone. The paper should be kept well-dampened to prevent clogging and scratching. Mineral spirits or a light oil may also be used as a lubricant when rubbing with water-

proof papers. The sandpaper should be used on a sanding block with a felt pad. Care must be taken not to cut through the finish, especially at the edges. Do not rub too long on any one spot, or the heat created from the friction may soften the varnish. Keep going over the work, coming back to rough spots later until all the work comes up to the desired smooth lustre. Wipe all traces of water or oil from the surface after rubbing.

Use of wax as a finishing material

One of the oldest methods of treating wood is with wax. Wax may be used as a complete finish starting with the bare wood, but more often it is used as a finishing coat over other types of finishes.

Wax finishes will not withstand excessive moisture or heat. The durability of a wax finish depends on the undercoats and the polishing, and in all cases periodic coats of wax and polishes must be applied to retain a good finish.

A good grade of paste wax should be used on furniture. Most of the better grades have a base of Brazilian wax, a product of the palm tree. Beeswax and paraffin waxes are also used.

The number of coats of wax required depends on the number of undercoats of other finishing materials used. Wax should be applied to the surface by spreading the paste wax between two pieces of cheesecloth and rubbing it on the work in a circular motion. Care must be taken to spread the wax evenly but thinly; it is much better to use several thin coats of wax than to use one thick coat. If the wax coat is thick, it is very difficult to polish.

Allow the wax to set for ten minutes, and then rub the surface briskly with a soft cloth. Rub in a circular motion at first and then with the grain. Let the work set for one hour before applying the second coat. Considerable rubbing

Fig. 25:1   Applying a Wax Finish

is required to bring the surface to a high polish. The polish can be tested by trying to put a thumb print on the surface; if it can be seen, more polishing is required.

Paints and enamels

Paints are one of our most decorative and versatile finishing materials. If they are properly mixed and applied, they provide an attractive and serviceable finish.

There have been many recent developments in the manufacture of paint, and through the use of chemicals many new kinds have become available, but the type still most used for furniture and trim has an oil base. Oil paint is made from mixing raw linseed oil with zinc oxide or white lead. Epoxy-based paints are now extensively used as they have a harder finish and can be applied over surfaces other than wood.

The colour in paint is provided by adding finely ground mineral pigments. Turpentine and Japan driers are also added as drying agents.

Enamels are made by mixing the coloured pigments with a varnish-based paint to provide a hard, shiny surface that can be rubbed in the same manner as a varnish or shellac finish, if desired.

Paints and enamels are not difficult to apply, but to produce a good professional finish these methods and precautions must be followed:

1. Make sure the work is smooth, clean, and free from all dirt, grease, or other foreign matter.

2. Fill all nail holes with putty or other suitable filler.

3. Cover all knots or streaks of pitchy wood with a coat of shellac to prevent them from showing through the paint.

4. Stir the paint thoroughly.

5. Use only clean, soft brushes.

6. It is important that the wood be perfectly dry; no paint will properly adhere to a wet surface.

7. The brush should be loaded lightly so that a thin but even coat can be spread on the work; do not allow the paint to run or build up.

8. Be thorough; do not miss any spots. Paint in the difficult parts first.

9. Sand the work lightly between coats with 2/0 sandpaper.

10. Most paints require twenty-four hours to dry between coats. If it is a quick-drying paint, follow the manufacturer's instructions.

11. On most work a coat of white primer is put on the bare wood as an undercoat or base for the coloured paint to follow.

12. When you use enamel, it may be left as a smooth, painted surface or, if a very fine finish is required you may rub it down as you would varnish.

Plain Fact

FINISHING MATERIALS WILL NOT HIDE YOUR MISTAKES BUT WILL GREATLY ENHANCE YOUR GOOD WORK.

Care of brushes

Any finish that is applied to wood can be no better than the brushes used to do the job. The proper care and storage of brushes will add greatly to the quality of your work.

Brushes must be suspended in a container so that the bristles do not rest on the bottom, or they will become curled and clogged with the sediment that settles at the bottom.

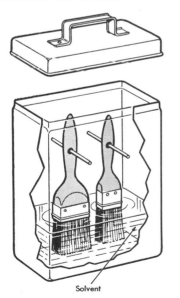

Solvent

Fig. 25:2 Holes Bored in Brushes to Fit Through Rods in Container

The type of solvent used in the brush container will depend on the type of material in which the brush has been used. Paint and oil varnish brushes can be stored in turpentine; shellac brushes in alcohol; lacquer brushes in alcohol or lacquer thinners. Brushes used for synthetic varnishes may require special solvents that are sold with the finishing materials. The solvents will not evaporate as rapidly if the container is closed. A suitable container is shown in Figure 25:2.

If the brush is not to be used again soon, it is better to clean the brush thoroughly in the proper solvent, dry it off, wrap it in newspaper, and store it in a dry place for future use.

ASSIGNMENT

Varnish

1. List the three classifications of varnishes and the ingredients of each type.
2. State the difference between spar varnish and rubbing varnish.
3. List one advantage of varnish made with synthetic resin over oil varnish.

185

4. What is the difference in the drying methods of oil varnish and spirit varnish?

5. (a) How are lacquers made?
   (b) How do they differ from oil or spirit varnish?

6. List the advantages and disadvantages of lacquer as a finishing material.

7. List the pointers that you consider most important when applying varnish.

8. Explain the difference between natural resins and synthetic resins (see Glossary of Terms).

Polyester finishes

9. How do polyester finishes differ from lacquer finishes?

10. Why is the catalyst added to the other two substances of the polyester material only immediately prior to its being used?

11. List the advantages and disadvantages of polyester finishes.

12. Define the terms *organic compound, reactive monomer, and molecule* (see Glossary of Terms).

Rubbing a finish

13. Why should a varnished finish be rubbed down?

14. List the materials that may be used to rub down a finish.

15. (a) Describe one method of rubbing the final coat with pumice stone.
    (b) How is silicon carbide sandpaper used for rubbing a finish?

Wax

16. What are some of the limitations of a wax finish?

17. What is the base of most paste wax?

18. Explain how wax should be applied to a surface.

19. How can you test a waxed surface to determine if it is sufficiently polished?

Paints and enamels

20. What are the ingredients of oil paints?

21. What is the difference between paint and enamel?

22. List four rules for painting that you consider important in producing a good job.

23. (a) How should paint brushes be stored?
    (b) What solvent should be used for oil varnish brushes? shellac brushes? paint brushes? lacquer brushes?

24. Give the complete finishing schedule, listing each step required, to finish a piece of birch furniture with a walnut varnish finish.

CHAPTER TWENTY-SIX

sharpening hand tools

A dull plane or a dull chisel is of no more value than a hammer with a broken handle, yet how often do we see students and even tradesmen attempting to work with them. Sharp tools are safer, more accurate, and much easier to use than dull ones. The time spent in sharpening tools will pay big dividends when you come to use them. The sharpening operation for most hand tools is relatively simple and can be done quickly once you have performed it on a few tools and have become familiar with it. Get into the habit of keeping your tools sharp; it will be of value to you as long as you use tools of any type.

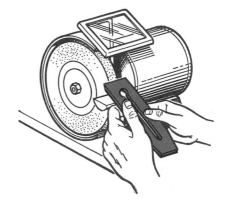

Fig. 26:1   Grinding a Plane Iron

How to sharpen a plane iron

The two operations required in sharpening a plane iron are:

(a) grinding the edge to the correct angle and shape, and

(b) honing the edge on an oil-stone. This operation is referred to as *whetting*.

Grinding

It is not necessary to grind the blade each time it is sharpened. Only when the blade is nicked or the bevel has become rounded should it be ground. The blade can generally be honed several times between grindings.

If the blade is to be ground, care must be taken to keep it cool by frequent quenchings in water. If the blade becomes overheated so that blue spots appear at the cutting edge, the temper will be removed, making the blade soft

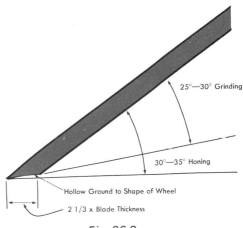

25°—30° Grinding

30°—35° Honing

Hollow Ground to Shape of Wheel

2 1/3 x Blade Thickness

Fig. 26:2

and easily dulled. The blade should be ground at an angle of from 25° to 30°. The correct angle can be estimated by making the bevelled edge 2⅓ times as long as the thickness of the blade (see Figure 26:2).

The honing or whetting operation

The oil-stone used to sharpen plane blades may be made from natural stone

187

or, more often, from artificial abrasives of either aluminum oxide or silicon carbide. They come in coarse, fine, and medium grits. Some stones have a coarse grit on one side and a fine grit on the other side. Oil-stones should be set into a block of wood so that they can be held firmly while in use.

A few drops of light oil should be used on the stone to float away the particles of steel. This will prevent the stone from becoming clogged.

Hone the bevelled edge of the blade first, holding it at a slightly steeper angle than the blade bevel so that most of the honing is done at the cutting edge. The blade may be moved back and forth the full length of the stone or it may be moved in a circular direction (see Figure 26:3A). After a few strokes on the bevelled side of the blade, turn it over so the back is flat on the stone. Give the blade a few strokes on the back, making sure that you do not raise the end. There should be absolutely no bevel on this side of the blade (see Figure 26:3B). Repeat these operations several times until the feather edge caused by grinding the blade is removed. Test the blade by touching it on the thumb nail. A few strokes on a leather strap will produce an even keener edge.

The blade should be very slightly rounded at the two edges, as shown in Figure 26:4, to prevent it from dig-

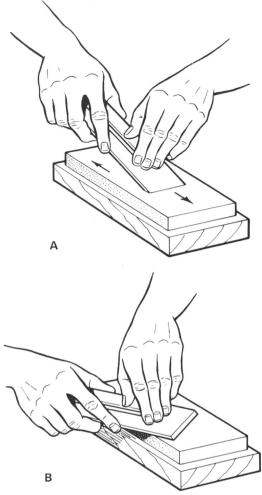

A

B

Fig. 26:3 Repeat these two operations until the feather edge is removed.

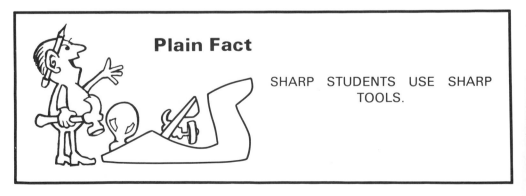

Plain Fact

SHARP STUDENTS USE SHARP TOOLS.

ging in and leaving plane marks on the finished work.

When reassembling the sharpened blade and plane iron cap, be careful not to dull the keen edge. They should be assembled as shown in Figures 26:5 to 26:7.

Chisels and other bevelled-edge cutting tools are sharpened in the same manner as the plane. However, the angle of the bevel may vary according to the use of the chisel: for rough work a larger angle, for fine work a smaller angle. In general, the 30° to 35° angle will make a good cut. When sharpening gouges, use a slip stone, which is made to fit the contour of curved blades. Such a stone is shown in Figure 26:8.

Remember, you are more apt to cut yourself with a dull chisel than a sharp one.

Stanley Tools

Fig. 26:6 Slide the plane iron cap up until it is ¹/₁₆″ from the cutting edge of the blade. Then tighten the screw.

Stanley Tools

Fig. 26:7 Plane Iron and Plane Iron Cap Assembled

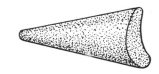

Fig. 26:8 Slip Stone

Round Corners Slightly

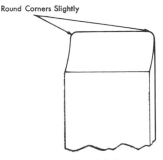

Fig. 26:4

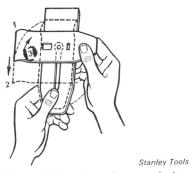

Stanley Tools

Fig. 26:5 To put the plane iron and the plane iron cap together, place the cap on the flat side of the blade with the screw in the lower part of the slot. Swing the cap around, making the edge parallel to the blade.

How to sharpen a scraper

The scraper operates with a combination of a cutting and a scraping action, removing the wood by moving a burred edge over the surface of the work. The burr is formed by making a sharp edge, or arris, and then bending or burring this edge over to make a cutting surface.

So that a straight and even burr can be formed on scrapers, they are made of a soft, mild steel. This makes it necessary to sharpen them often, as the mild steel will not hold a sharp cutting edge very long. It is, therefore, important that you know how to sharpen scrapers if you are to use them efficiently. The procedure is as follows:

189

1. Remove the old burr by placing the scraper flat on a bench and filing it, as shown in Figure 26:9.

2. With the scraper in an upright position in a vise, draw-file the edge square and straight; use a smooth mill file. Hold the file in a horizontal position (see Figure 26:10).

3. Whet the edge just filed to make corners that are perfectly smooth and square. Hold the blade in an upright position, as shown in Figure 26:11.

4. Remove the slight burr formed on the edge during filing and whetting, by rubbing it flat on the stone, as shown in Figure 26:12.

5. With a burnisher (a hardened steel oval-shaped tool), draw the edge with a few strokes, as shown in Figure 26:13.

6. The edge should now be ready to be turned over to form the desired cutting edge. To do this, place the blade in the vise as shown, and with the

Fig. 26:9 File off the old burr.

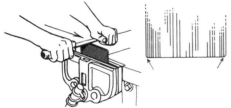

Fig. 26:10 Draw-file the edge of a scraper.

Fig. 26:11 Whet the edge by holding the scraper at a right angle to the face of the oil-stone.

Fig. 26:12 Remove the small burr by whetting the blade on the face.

Fig. 26:13 Hold the burnisher flat on the scraper blade. Press down and draw back and forth several times.

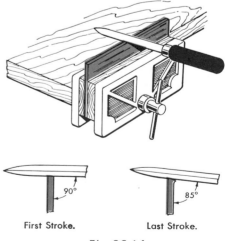

First Stroke.   Last Stroke.

Fig. 26:14

190

burnisher in a horizontal position, press down firmly, drawing the burnisher across the scraper. With each stroke, lower the handle slightly until the burnisher is at approximately 85° to the face of the blade (see Figure 26:14).

7. Turn the scraper around and repeat operation 6. This will give you two cutting edges.

Since the scraper blades must be made from a very mild steel so that a burr can be easily formed, they soon dull and require repeated sharpenings. However, after you have sharpened a hand scraper a few times you will be able to get a good cutting edge quickly and easily.

Cabinet scrapers and scraper plane blades must be sharpened in the same manner as a plane blade. After this has been done, the burnisher is placed with the edge resting on the bevel and slid across the blade. The handle is tilted down further on each stroke until a good cutting burr is formed (see Figure 26:15).

How to sharpen a hand saw

Saw sharpening requires a knowledge of hand saw types and the shape and size of their teeth as well as the types of saw files and saw sets, and the methods of using them. With this knowledge, patience, and practice, anyone can sharpen hand saws.

A good hand saw is made from a well-tempered piece of tool steel that tapers from the back to the cutting edge and from the handle to the point. The teeth should be even on top, uniform in size, and so shaped as to cut on the push stroke with sharp points and cutting edges. The hand saw is a most effective and useful tool if properly sharpened and properly used.

The first operation in sharpening either a rip saw or a cross-cut saw is

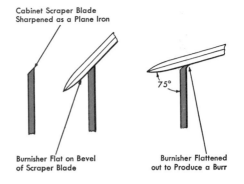

Cabinet Scraper Blade
Sharpened as a Plane Iron

75°

Burnisher Flat on Bevel
of Scraper Blade

Burnisher Flattened
out to Produce a Burr

Fig. 26:15 Cabinet Scraper Blade

to *joint* the teeth. This is done by placing the saw in a saw vise and laying a flat mill file over the teeth lengthwise and sliding it along the full length of the saw. Continue until the tops of the high teeth have been filed down to the level of the tops of the lowest teeth (see Figure 26:16). This will make all the teeth the same height and the flats thus formed will act as a guide when sharpening the points on the teeth.

After jointing, the saw should be *set*. The purpose of the set is to give the blade clearance by making the saw cut slightly wider than the thickness of the blade. This is done by bending the teeth

Fig. 26:16 Jointing the Top of the Teeth

191

outward, each tooth in the opposite direction to its neighbour. A saw set is used for this operation. Several types are on the market, one of which is shown in Figure 26:17. It must be adjusted for the required set for the size of teeth of the saw. From one side of the blade, set every other tooth outward (see Figure 26:18). Reverse the saw in the vise and set the alternate teeth; be sure every tooth is set. Only the upper half of the tooth should be set because the tooth may break if too deep a set is made.

Before starting to file the cutting edge of the teeth, you must have a clear picture of the shape of the correctly formed teeth on the rip saw and the cross-cut saw.

For sharpening hand saws a three-cornered, slim, or extra-slim tapered file should be used. The coarser the saw the longer the file should be. The file sizes generally used on most hand saws are the 6", 7", and 8" lengths. The longer the file the larger the cross-section of the file will be.

Sharpening the cross-cut saw teeth

The cross-cut saw teeth are sharpened so that a scoring cut across the grain

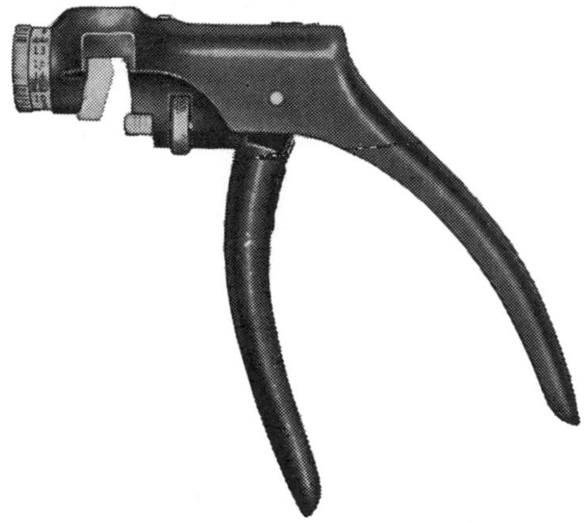

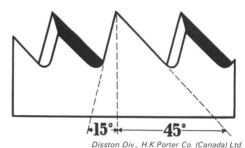

Disston Div., H.K.Porter Co. (Canada) Ltd.
Fig. 26:19 Side View of Cross-cut Teeth (Enlarged)

Stanley Tools
Fig. 26:17 Saw Set

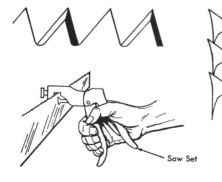

Fig. 26:18 Cross-cut Teeth (Set)

Disston Div., H.H.Porter Co. (Canada) Ltd.
Fig. 26:20 Edge View of Cross-cut Teeth

will be made on the push stroke. To produce this cutting edge on the teeth, place the saw in a saw vise with the handle to the right, as shown in Figure 26:23. Place the file in the gullet to the left of the first tooth that is bent toward you. Hold the file in a horizontal position and at 60° to the face of the saw. Some saw filers prefer to tip the handle end of the file from 5° to 10° from the horizontal. Set the file well down in the gullet and let it find its own bearing. You will find it a help if you observe the shape and angle of some of the unused teeth that are always at the toe of the blade. Slide the file across the blade so that it files the back of the

tooth to the left and the front of the tooth to the right on the same stroke. The file should always cut on the push stroke. File until half the flat left on the tooth by jointing disappears. This will generally take two or three strokes. Now, lift the file and place it in the second gullet to the right, skipping one gullet.

Repeat the filing operation, making sure to hold the file at the same angle. Carry on in the same manner, placing the file in every second gullet until the handle is reached.

Reverse the saw in the vise with the handle to the left, as shown in Figure 26:24. Place the file in the first gullet

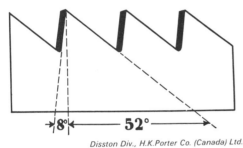

Disston Div., H.K.Porter Co. (Canada) Ltd.

Fig. 26:21 Side View of Rip Teeth (Enlarged)

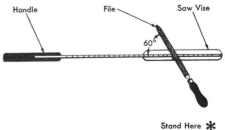

Fig. 26:23 First Position for Filing a Crosscut Saw. File may be held 10° off the horizontal.

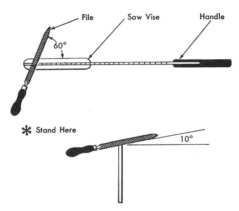

Fig. 26:24 Second Position for Filing Crosscut Saw

Disston Div., H.K.Porter Co. (Canada) Ltd.

Fig. 26:22 Edge View of Rip Teeth

193

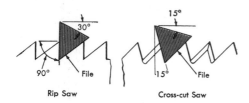

Fig. 26:25 Position of File to Obtain the Correct Hook on Rip and Cross-cut teeth

in from the toe end of the blade. This should be the first gullet that was skipped when you filed from the opposite side of the saw. File at the same angle as before and until the other half of the flat disappears from the top of the tooth and it has a sharp point. Continue filing every other gullet until the handle is reached.

Inspect the saw to see if all teeth are sharpened to a point and are all the same size. If the teeth are of unequal size, the saw should be rejointed and filed.

To make the saw cut on the down stroke, a hook angle is filed on the teeth. That is, the teeth are shaped to dig in on the down stroke, as shown in Figure 26:25. The top of the file should be tilted from 15° to 20° for cross-cut saws and from 30° to 40° for rip saws.

Rip saw teeth are filed in the same manner as cross-cut teeth with the exception that the file should be held at right angles to the face of the saw and in a horizontal position.

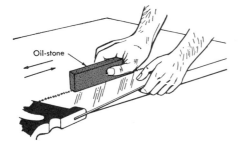

Fig. 26:26 Side Dressing the Teeth

The saw blade should be side dressed after filing to even up the set and to remove any burrs caused from filing. Place the saw flat on the bench and rub with an oil-stone, as shown in Figure 26:26.

ASSIGNMENT

Sharpening a plane or chisel

1. What are the two operations required for sharpening a plane iron?
2. At what angle should a plane iron be ground?
3. Why should you not allow the plane blade to become overheated during grinding?
4. From what materials are oil-stones made?
5. Why is oil used on the stone?
6. Explain the honing operation used for sharpening a plane iron.
7. What is the last operation in sharpening a plane iron?
8. How does the sharpening of a chisel to be used for rough work differ from the sharpening of one to be used for fine work?
9. How is a gouge chisel sharpened?
10. Why are you more apt to cut yourself with a dull chisel than with a sharp one?
11. Define the terms aluminum oxide and silicon carbide as they refer to oil-stones (see Glossary of Terms).

Scrapers

12. What is the principle of the cutting operation of a scraper?
13. Explain how the cutting edge is formed on a hand scraper blade.
14. How does a hand scraper blade differ from a cabinet scraper blade?

15. Why are scraper blades made from mild steel?

Sharpening a hand saw

16. What knowledge is required to be able to sharpen saws properly?

17. What is the purpose of jointing a hand saw before it is sharpened?

18. Why are the teeth of the saw set? What is the name of the tool used for this operation?

19. What types and lengths of files are used for sharpening hand saws?

20. Describe the correct position in which you should hold the file when sharpening a cross-cut saw tooth.

21. Why file only every other tooth from one side of the cross-cut saw?

22. Why should you cut away only half the flat on the tooth when filing from the first side of the saw?

23. What is meant by the hook of a saw tooth? How is it made in this shape?

24. How does the filing of a rip saw differ from the filing of a cross-cut saw?

25. What is meant by "side dressing a saw"? How is it done?

portable electric hand tools

Power tools not only supply the muscles for most woodworking operations; they make the work more interesting, get the job done faster, and get it done more accurately. Power tools do not think; that you must do for yourself. In fact, you must be more alert when using portable power tools than when using hand tools. Because of the speed and power of the equipment there is a greater safety hazard involved, and more accuracy and skill is necessary.

By using portable power tools and the attachments made to fit them you can perform almost any woodworking operation. Portable sanders and the router have already been discussed in Chapters 16 and 18 respectively. We will describe here some of the other portable power tools that are in general use. You should be familiar with them and know how to use them.

The portable electric hand drill

Of all portable power tools the drill is used by more tradesmen, students, and home-owners than any other tool. Nothing has done more to assist amateur craftsmen and home repair artists than the portable electric drill. It is light but durable, easy to handle, and ideal for drilling holes in wood, metal, and most other materials. With the proper attachments drills can be used for sanding, sawing, grinding, buffing, polishing, driving screws, and even stirring paint.

There are many types and sizes of portable electric drills, the ¼" and ⅜" drills being the most commonly used for light work. The size of the drill is determined by the shank of the largest

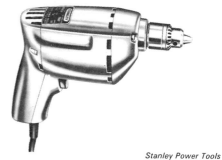

Stanley Power Tools

Fig. 27:1 ¼" Electric Drill

size of drill bit that will fit into the chuck. The size may also be indicated by the horsepower rating. Figure 27:1 illustrates a typical ¼" drill. The main components of a portable drill are the frame (usually of an aluminum alloy), the motor, the switch, the chuck, and the handle. Two larger drills, which are used for heavier work in construction or industry, are shown in Figures 27:2 and 27:3.

For drilling small holes (up to ⅜") in wood, use a standard twist bit the same as you would use for drilling metal. Larger holes can be bored with a dou-

Stanley Power Tools

Fig. 27:2 ½" Heavy Duty Electric Drill

Stanley Power Tools

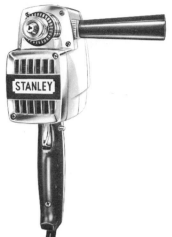

Fig. 27:3 ½" Heavy Duty Right Angle Drill

ble-spur, Forstner, or centre bit, such as those illustrated in Figures 15:3 to 15:6. For larger holes, those from 1¼" to 4", some type of cutter should be used. The two most often used are the hole saw and the fly cutter (see Figures 27:4 and 27:5).

The better electric drills have a variable-speed arrangement which enables the rpm of the chuck to be altered for the drilling of various types of materials and also for the different sizes of bits

Stanley Power Tools

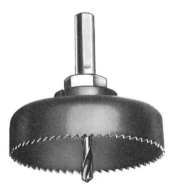

Fig. 27:4 Hole Saw for Use in an Electric Portable Drill or Drill Press

Stanley Power Tools

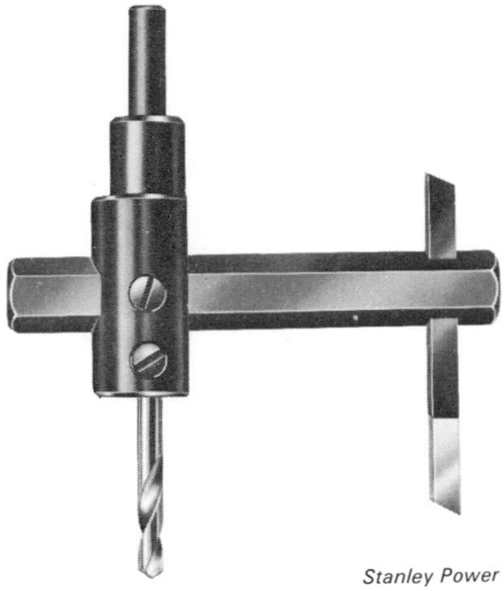

Fig. 27:5 Fly Cutter

or cutters. In general, the larger the hole the slower should be the speed of the drill. The variable-speed reversible-drive electric drill is also very handy when driving or removing wood screws.

How to use an electric hand drill

Hand drills are one of the simplest power tools to use, but the job can be made safer and easier if the following procedures are followed:

1. Accurately locate the position of the hole to be drilled. If the hole is to be drilled in wood, use a scratch awl; if in metal, use a centre punch.
2. Hold the drill securely and at the correct angle to the work surface.
3. If the hole is to be drilled at an angle of other than 90°, it is a good idea to make a jig consisting of a block of wood with a hole drilled through it at the desired angle. The block can then be clamped to the work to serve as a guide and to prevent the drill from sliding off the starting-point.
4. Use a back-up block to prevent the underside of the work from splintering when the drill breaks through.
5. Do not shut off the drill until the bit has been withdrawn from the hole.

Safety precautions for electric hand drills

1. Use only a grounded electrical outlet and cord.

2. If the work is small, it should be clamped to the bench.

3. If a variable-speed drill is being used, be sure the bit or cutter is travelling at the correct rpm for the work being drilled.

4. Hold the drill securely, especially when a large drill bit is used. The work must be clamped to a bench if a hole saw or fly cutter is used, because they occasionally stick or grab. When this happens the torque of the motor may cause the work to spin if it is not secured.

Portable electric hand saws

The electric tool that has been the biggest labour saver and has made many difficult jobs easy is the power saw. Almost any cut that can be made with a hand saw can be made with a power saw, more accurately, a great deal faster, and with much less effort. When you first use an electric saw you begin to realize what can be done with power tools and how they can be used to your advantage. If this power is treated with respect by observing some important safety rules, you can save a great deal of time and effort and still work effectively and safely.

Portable power saws are made in various sizes and weights. Because these saws are portable, and in many cases must be lifted to head height for vertical cuts, they are made as light as possible (from 6 to 12 pounds for most models), but sufficiently rugged to stand up to continuous heavy use. The frames are generally made from either aluminum alloy or light steel. The size of the saw is determined by the maximum diameter of blade that can be mounted

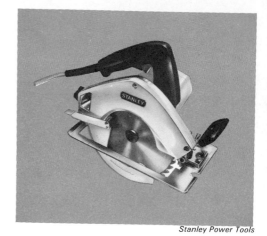

Stanley Power Tools

Fig. 27:6 8" Portable Electric Saw

on the spindle. Blade diameters range from 4" to 12", with the 7" and 8" sizes the most popular. For cutting wood the cross-cut, rip saw, combination, and planer blades are used. Special blades or abrasive discs are used for cutting such materials as ceramic tile, slate, concrete, asbestos, plastic, light sheet steel, or almost any other construction material.

A typical portable power saw is shown in Figure 27:6. The base of the saw is equipped with a rip saw fence to use as a guide for long ripping cuts (see Figure 27:7). There is generally a

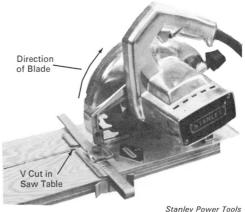

Direction of Blade

V Cut in Saw Table

Stanley Power Tools

Fig. 27:7 Rip Saw Fence

V-shaped notch at the front of the saw base that is in line with the saw blade. If the centre of this V follows the layout line, a straight cut can be made for either cross-cutting or rip sawing. The saw base is adjustable so that the depth of the cut can be varied. It can also be tilted to allow angles, bevels, or chamfers to be cut.

The portable electric saw will not replace the conventional table saw either for accuracy or for ease of operations. Its value is in its portability; the saw is taken to the work rather than the work to the saw.

How to use a portable electric saw

1. Draw guide lines at the desired location of the cut.

2. Use the correct blade for the material or cut to be made.

3. Adjust the depth and angle of the blade to suit the cut to be made.

4. Hold the handle of the saw firmly, with the forefinger operating the trigger switch, and the other hand on the stock, well away from the cutting line. For some saws and some cutting operations both hands are required on the machine.

5. Place the base of the saw on the work and align the V-shaped guide mark with the layout line. Press the switch and allow the motor to reach full speed before feeding it into the cut.

6. Use the saw guide when possible. If a long cut is to be made in plywood, a straightedge should be clamped to it and used in place of the rip guide.

7. Cut on the waste side of the line. Do not stand directly behind the cutting line.

Safety precautions for electric saws

Portable electric saws are efficient tools but are also a potential source of danger if not handled with care. No person should operate a portable saw until instructed in its use.

1. Connect the saw only to grounded electrical outlets.

2. Most portable saws are equipped with spring-loaded telescoping guards that should spring back over the blade after the wood has been cut. Make sure this guard operates freely at all times.

3. Use the correct blade, and make sure it is assembled on the saw with the teeth pointing up on the forward edge.

4. Use only sharp blades. A saw with a dull blade will have to be forced and this will discolour the wood, and overheat the blade and cause it to stall.

5. Make sure all adjustments are tight.

6. When operating the saw hold it firmly and avoid careless handling of the saw or the work.

7. Do not cross-cut a board between two supporting points. It will cause the blade to bind and may throw the saw out of control.

8. Always wear safety goggles when using a metal-cutting blade or an abrasive disc on the saw.

Many accidents occur from over-confidence. A portable power saw, even after you have used it for some time, demands all your attention.

Sabre saw

The sabre saw is a relatively easy and safe saw to use, and though it is sometimes considered as a hobby tool, there are many uses for this very versatile tool in woodworking shops and on construction. A typical sabre saw is shown in Figure 27:8.

Stanley Power Tools

Fig. 27:8   Sabre Saw

The portable scroll or sabre saw has a narrow stiff blade that moves up and down allowing it to cut curves and intricate patterns. It can do much the same work as a jig saw, but has the advantage of being portable so that it can be taken to the work. Any length of stock or any radius or angle can be cut. The cuts may be made at a right angle to the surface or at any angle up to 45° by adjusting the tilting saw base (see Figure 27:9).

In spite of its light weight (generally about 5 pounds), the sabre saw is a rugged tool. It can be fitted with various types of blades that will cut wood up to 2" thick, and will also cut such mate-

rials as aluminum, brass, and light steel, as well as plastic, leather, and asbestos.

How to use a sabre saw

1. Make heavy layout lines for the pattern to be cut. Never cut freehand.

2. Use the proper blade for the type and thickness of the material as well as for the radius to be cut.

3. Install the blade correctly and make sure all adjustments are tight.

4. When cutting, hold the saw firmly, pressing forward and downward. If the work is small, clamp it to a bench or secure it in a vise.

5. Cut on the waste side of the line. If straight cuts are to be made, clamp a straightedge to the work to act as a rip-cut fence.

6. When making internal cuts, bore a hole larger than the width of the blade to start the cut.

Safety precautions for sabre saws

1. Before adjusting or changing the blade, make sure the saw is disconnected.

2. Hold the saw and the work so that

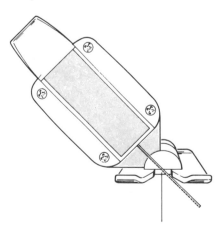
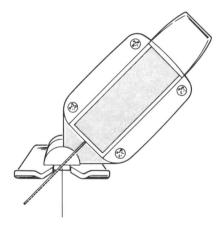

Fig. 27:9   Angle Cutting with a Sabre Saw

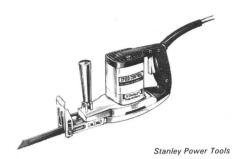

Stanley Power Tools

Fig. 27:10 General-Purpose Saw

your fingers are well away from the blade and the cutting line.

3. Before removing the saw from the work, turn off the switch. There is danger of breaking the blade if the end strikes the work while the saw is being removed with the blade still in motion.

Several heavier, general-purpose saws are made with a blade that has an up-and-down action; these saws are extensively used in building construction. They are not used for cutting curves, although the base can be tilted to make angle cuts, because the blade is too wide. They are used for heavy work and with special blades that will cut through all kinds of materials, such as wood, nails, plaster, metal, and plastic pipe. A general-purpose saw is shown in Figure 27:10.

ASSIGNMENT

1. Why should you be more alert when operating power tools than when using hand tools?

Portable drill

2. List six operations besides drilling holes that can be performed with an electric drill.

3. What factor determines the size of an electric drill?

4. Name three types of bits and two types of cutters used for boring large holes in wood.

5. What is meant by *variable speed* as it relates to an electric drill?

6. What arrangement can be used to make it easier to drill a hole in wood at an angle?

7. What precautions must be taken when cutting a hole in a piece of wood with a fly cutter?

Portable saw

8. How is the size of an electric portable saw determined? What is the most popular size?

9. (a) List four types of blades used for cutting wood. (b) What cutting arrangement is generally used in place of a blade for cutting most non-wood materials?

10. What is the purpose of the two adjustments on the base of the portable saw?

11. Read again the points listed under "How to use an electric portable saw" and list the three points you consider the most important.

12. List four safety precautions that must be observed when operating an electric power saw.

Sabre saw

13. Explain the cutting action of a sabre saw.

14. List four pointers concerning the use of the sabre saw that should help you to do a good job.

15. List three safety precautions that must be observed while operating the sabre saw.

16. (a) How does the general-purpose saw differ from the sabre saw? (b) If the proper blades are used, what type of material can be cut with the general-purpose saw?

CHAPTER TWENTY-EIGHT

laminating and bending

Laminating

In modern furniture and cabinetmaking it is often desirable to make curved or irregularly shaped members. In some cases it is possible to bend or band-saw the solid stock to the required shape. However, it is generally more desirable to glue several layers of thin wood into a single permanent shape. This operation is referred to as *laminating*. The thin layers of wood are called *laminas*. When properly laminated, these sections will retain their shapes and be stronger than if they were cut or bent from solid stock of comparable size (see Figure 28:1). Figure 28:2 shows an example of chair members made by bonding thin laminas of stock together, with the grain of all pieces running in the same direction, a method that makes them much stronger than if they had been band-sawn to shape from solid stock. Because of their strength and adaptability to modern design, laminated members are being extensively used in cabinetmaking and furniture making, as well as in sports equipment, farm implements, and structural members.

When a laminated curved member is used in place of two or more solid pieces, there is a saving of time because no mortise-and-tenon or other wood joints are required, and an attractive and strong type of construction is still produced.

The sharpness of the bend that can be made depends on several factors: (a) the thickness of the wood; (b) the species of wood; (c) the moisture content of the wood; (d) the equipment used to form the bends.

Both softwoods and hardwoods can be bent, but hardwoods have better bending characteristics than softwoods. Hardwoods that are used for either solid or laminated bending are birch, ash, hickory, oak, and maple. Softwoods, such as Douglas fir, cedar, pine and redwood, are used for laminated structural beams or arches, such as those used in churches, arenas, and some homes. It is important that good-quality lumber be used, with straight grain, and free of knots, checks, splits, or other defects.

Large laminated curved sections are made with the grain of alternate layers running at right angles or diagonally to

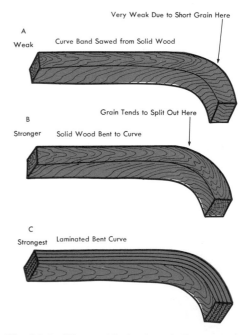

Very Weak Due to Short Grain Here

A
Weak — Curve Band Sawed from Solid Wood

Grain Tends to Split Out Here

B
Stronger — Solid Wood Bent to Curve

C
Strongest — Laminated Bent Curve

Fig. 28:1 Three Methods of Forming a Curved Section

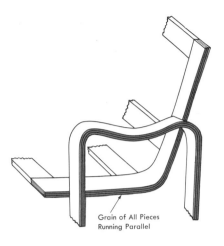

Fig. 28:2   Laminated Chair Members

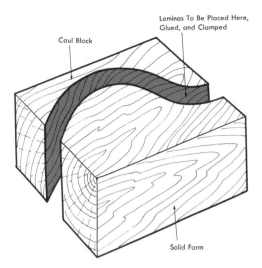

Fig. 28:3   Form and Caul Block

each other. These shapes are referred to as *moulded plywood*. Boat hulls are a good example of this type of laminated construction. The makeup of many moulded plywood members is the same as that of ordinary plywood, which consists of a centre core ply with a layer of thin crossband ply on either side of it with the grain running at right angles to the core, and a thin face veneer on the outside of each of these layers, with the grain running the same as the core. The core and the crossbands are often made of poplar or other inexpensive woods.

When bonding together curved or irregular shaped laminas, special gluing or bending equipment is required. First, a solid form must be made up to the desired shape of the piece required. A *caul block* is then made to match the shape of the solid form and the part to be fabricated (see Figure 28:3). In some cases, where a large radius is involved,

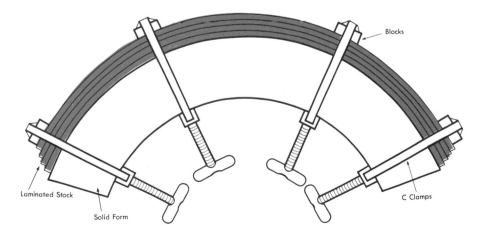

Fig. 28:4   Laminating Curved Members without the Use of a Caul Block

the wood may be clamped to the solid form without the aid of the matching caul, but small protective blocks should be used under the clamps (see Figure 28:4).

The fact that the thin layers and the glued joints are visible on the edge of laminated sections is sometimes considered to be a disadvantage of this type of construction. However, if the lamination is well made and the edge properly finished, the glued joints need not detract from the appearance of the work.

The strips of wood to be glued should be cut to the correct width and to a thickness that will allow them to be easily bent around the form. The matching faces of the strips should be planed smooth.

For best results use urea resin glue; it dries slowly enough to provide ample assembly time and cures in twenty-four hours (much faster if heat is applied).

For most laminated sections some form of caul block is used to ensure a well-fitting glue joint. Where large sections are made, some type of press or fixture is often necessary in order to get the pressure in the centre of the section. The pressure is generally applied in the centre first, squeezing the glue to the outer edges; this prevents glue pockets forming between the laminas. An improvised press for this purpose is shown in Figure 28:5. Narrower members may be laminated in a simple form and caul block, as illustrated in Figure 28:6. The forms and caul blocks may be made of solid stock or of several pieces of ¾" plywood, or they may be made as shown in Figure 28:7.

Bending

There are two other methods of bending wood when curved pieces are required: (a) by making relief cuts in solid stock; or (b) by steaming.

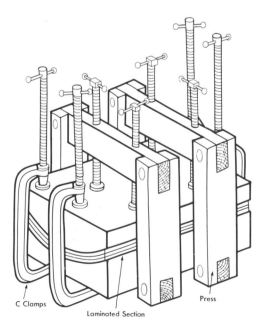

C Clamps

Laminated Section

Press

Fig. 28:5   Laminating Press

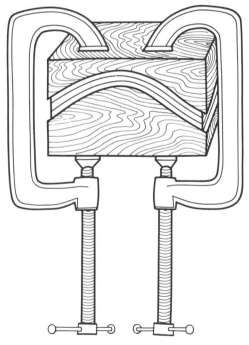

Fig. 28:6   Solid Form and Caul Block for Narrow Laminated Member

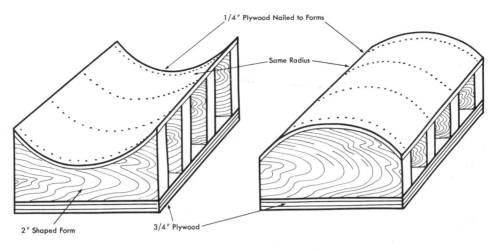

Fig. 28:7   Built-up Laminating Forms

It is often more economical to bend a solid section by making relief cuts in the back of it than to obtain the necessary forms and caul blocks required to make a laminated piece. This is especially true if appearance rather than strength is the main concern. The relief cuts are made at intervals depending on the sharpness of the bend to be made. All cuts must be of uniform depth and spacing. The smaller the radius, the closer the cuts should be. To add strength, glue can be placed in the saw cuts and a thin strip of wood glued to the inside curve.

When sharp bends in solid pieces are required, the wood should be steamed to make the fibres more pliable. A steam box can be improvised from pipe and a wooden box to suit a given purpose. After removing the piece from the steam box it should be clamped to a form of a somewhat smaller radius than the desired curve; this will allow for spring-back. For best results, only live steam should be in contact with the wood. The wood must remain clamped to the form until it is thoroughly dry, or

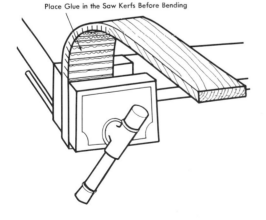

Fig. 28:8   Place glue in the saw kerfs before bending.

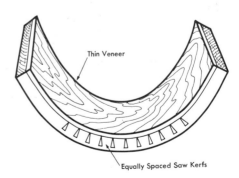

Fig. 28:9   Bending Wood Using Saw Kerfs

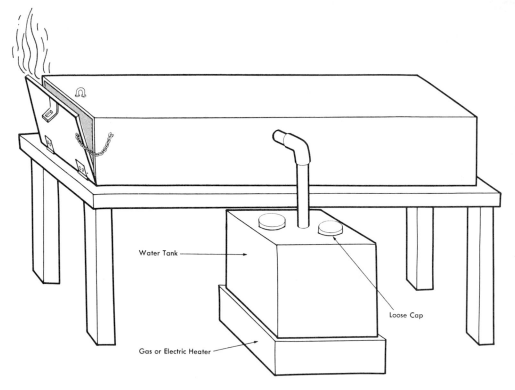

Fig. 28:10 Improvised Steam Cabinet

Use also a caul block and clamp if necessary.

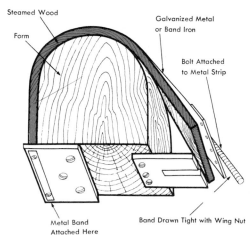

Fig. 28:11 Form for Forming Steamed Members

it will not retain its shape.

When the bend is sharp and there is some danger of the fibres splitting out at the outside radius of a bend, a galvanized strip can be clamped to the piece and bent with the wood, as shown in Figure 28:11.

ASSIGNMENT

1. What is meant by a *laminated member*?

2. State the advantage of using a laminated curved piece rather than a solid band-sawn one.

3. What special equipment is required for making a laminated curved member?

4. What, if any, is the disadvantage of using laminated pieces of furniture?

5. Make a sketch of the forms and cauls required to make the laminated section shown below.

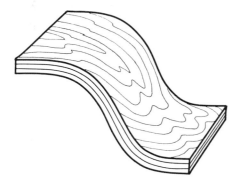

6. Describe the operation of forming a curved section by making relief cuts.

7. When sharp bends are to be made in solid stock, why is the wood steamed?

8. After steaming, why are the pieces clamped to forms until they are thoroughly dry?

cabinet and furniture details

The term *cabinet* refers to any type of enclosed chest, set of drawers, or cupboard that may be fitted with doors, bins, shelves, or drawers. Generally cabinets form storage or service units and are fixed in place in homes, offices, stores, and other commercial buildings.

Furniture, on the other hand, comprises the more portable household items, such as tables, chairs, beds, and desks, that are not attached to a building and do not form a part of it. There is, however, considerable overlap in the method of construction, the parts, and the terminology of cabinets and furniture.

Many of the construction details for both furniture and cabinet work are more or less standard, although the development of new materials and techniques is making changes in these details necessary. Be on the lookout for such new materials as plastics and special hardboards and hardware, and how they are being incorporated into furniture and cabinet construction.

Some of the materials used for cabinet work are (a) solid wood (either in single pieces or several pieces glued together); (b) particle board (made from wood chips); (c) hardboard (tightly compressed wood fibres); (d) plywood; and (e) plastic-coated materials such as those used for counter tops and some table tops.

Cabinets

Cabinets consist of several basic parts, one of these being the end section, sometimes referred to as the *gable* and sometimes as the *end frame*. The gables may be made of solid glued-up

stock or plywood, or of stiles, rails, and panels, as in Figure 29:4. They are attached to the front frames and other members by mitre, rabbet, or butt joints, and may have a rabbeted or square edge to receive the cabinet back. The top, shelves, and base are fitted into the cabinet ends with dado joints.

Shelves may be permanently attached in dado joints, as in Figure 29:1, or they may be made adjustable by installing shelf hardware, which consists of metal strips with equally spaced slots, sometimes called *pilaster* strips. Clips are inserted in the slots at the desired positions (see Figure 29:2).

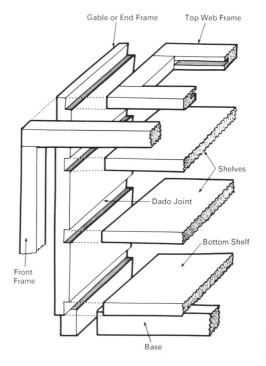

Gable or End Frame   Top Web Frame

Shelves

Dado Joint

Bottom Shelf

Front Frame

Base

Fig. 29:1   Gable, Shelves, and Frames

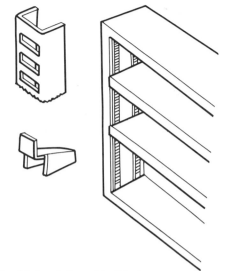

Fig. 29:2 Adjustable Shelves

the solid, glued-up frames. Plywood has the advantage that it is made in large sheets and in a wide range of thicknesses and face veneers, and it will hold its shape with a minimum of twisting, warping, or swelling. The principal disadvantage of plywood is that the exposed edges must be covered with solid wood strip or tape to improve their appearance.

Composition board frames

These frames are made from platewood or other kinds of fibre board with a hardwood face veneer, and have the same advantages and disadvantages as plywood frames.

The three types described above are solid end frames. An example of such a frame is shown in Figure 29:1.

The cabinet top may be attached to the gables by mitre, dado, or rabbet joints, or it may be set on top with a projecting overhang. The top should be screwed and glued to the ends, front, and supporting frames. Several methods of fastening the top are shown in Figure 29:3.

Cabinet frames

The basic framework of a cabinet, consisting of the top, ends, base, and frames, is referred to as *case construction*. The type of frame used will depend on the design of the cabinet and the material from which it is to be made. Some of the frames used are described below:

Solid wood frames

Solid ¾" stock glued edge to edge makes strong frames that can be easily finished and require no special edge treatment. However, they sometimes warp or swell in humid conditions.

Plywood frames

These are extensively used for cabinet work and are to a large extent replacing

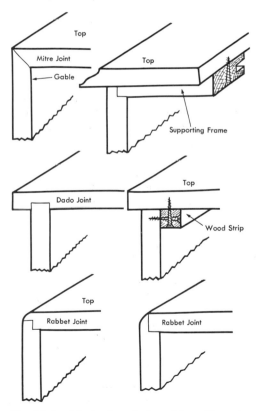

Fig. 29:3 Methods of Attaching Top to Frames or Gables

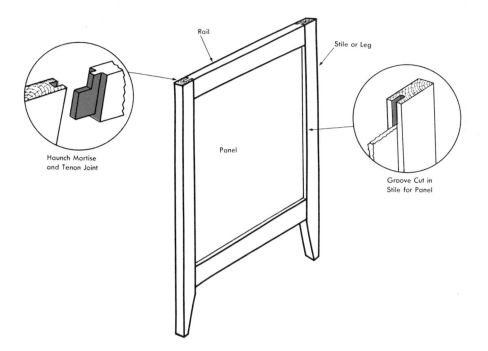

Fig. 29:4 Panel End Frame

Panel frames

These frames are generally made up of stiles (which, in the case of end frames, may also serve as legs), top and bottom rails, and thin plywood panels. Panel frames are light in weight but strong enough to support doors, drawers, and shelves if guides and cleats are attached to the stiles or legs. A panel frame is shown in Figure 29:4.

Skeleton frames

Sometimes called *web frames*, they are used as supporting members and guides for drawers and are placed in a horizontal position, generally between the drawer and shelf sections of a cabinet (see Figure 29:5).

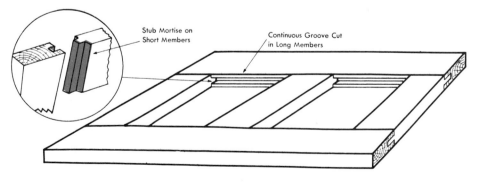

Fig. 29:5 Skeleton Frame

Front frames

Front frames are similar to skeleton frames. They are made up of the front face members on which the doors are hinged and, in general, make up the front trim of the cabinet (see Figure 29:1). If these members are made up as a frame, mortise-and-tenon joints are used to join the members together. In some cases these members are attached individually to the front edges of the other frames, making a large front frame unnecessary.

Frames may be made of materials other than wood, such as plastics, fibre

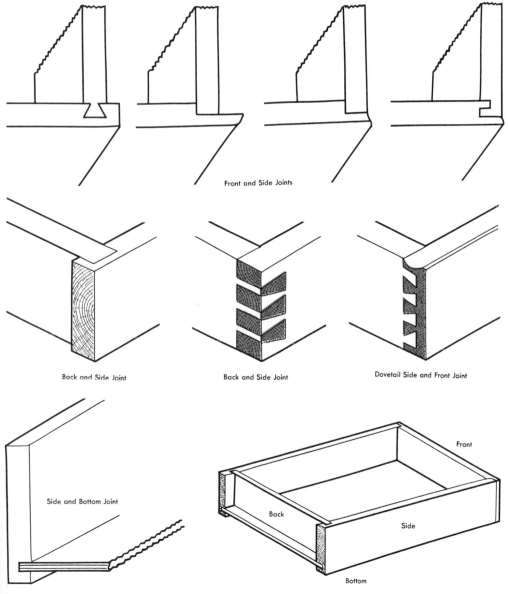

Front and Side Joints

Back and Side Joint

Back and Side Joint

Dovetail Side and Front Joint

Side and Bottom Joint

Front

Back

Side

Bottom

Fig. 29:6 A Simple Drawer Construction

glass, aluminum, and other metals. They may also be a combination of wood and other materials, with a plastic panel and wood rails or legs.

Drawer construction

There are two general types of cabinet drawers: (a) the *flush drawer*, which has a front that is flush with the face of the cabinet; and (b) the *lipped drawer* with a front that extends over the front cabinet members.

The flush drawers are more often used in furniture such as desks and chests, while the lipped drawers are frequently used for kitchen or colonial furniture. More precision is required in making and fitting the flush type drawers if they are to fit and look neat and yet be free-moving.

Drawers should be made from a good grade of well-seasoned lumber. The fronts should be of the same material as the face of the cabinet, usually ¾" thick. The sides and the back of the drawers may be of less expensive wood ⅝" thick, while the bottom is generally made from ¼" plywood or composition hardboard.

Several different wood joints are used in drawer construction, the ones used depending on the type of cabinet being built. Figure 29:6 illustrates several of the common ones.

Drawers must have sufficient clearance to allow them to run smoothly, but not so much that they are loose and sloppy. There should be ⅛" clearance in height and ³⁄₁₆" in width. A stop should be attached to the back of the cabinet to stop the drawer when the front is flush with the front of the cabinet.

All joints should be glued and nailed. Make sure the drawer is flat and square before the glue sets.

There are several types of drawer slides and guides, the type used depending on the style of the cabinet, and the size of the drawer. Figure 29:7 illustrates several guide arrangements.

Cabinet doors

There are two basic types of cabinet doors: *swinging* and *sliding*. Both types can be of either the panel or the solid flush design. The present trend is to the flush type made from plywood, composition board, or solid wood.

Swinging doors

Swinging doors may be hinged from the side, either as single doors or in pairs, or on occasion cabinet doors may be hinged at the top or bottom to swing either up or down. They may also be hinged to each other in accordion style, as shown in Figure 29:8.

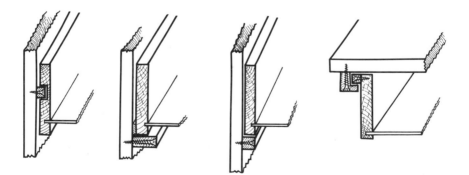

Fig. 29:7 Drawer Slide and Guide Arrangements. Several types of metal drawer guides with rollers are manufactured to make the operation of the drawers easier.

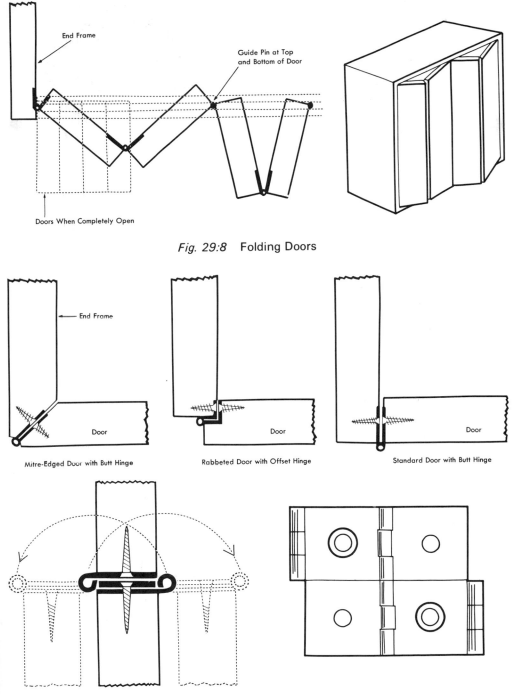

Fig. 29:8   Folding Doors

Mitre-Edged Door with Butt Hinge

Rabbeted Door with Offset Hinge

Standard Door with Butt Hinge

Double-Action Hinge

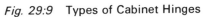

Fig. 29:9   Types of Cabinet Hinges

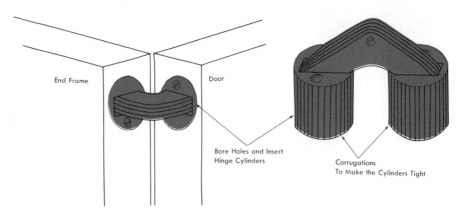

Fig. 29:10 Invisible Hinge

The size and weight of the door as well as the design of the cabinet should determine the hinges selected. Several types of hinges are described in Chapter 21; others are illustrated in Figures 29:9 and 29:10.

Cabinet doors should be fitted to allow $1/16''$ clearance at top, bottom, and sides to allow for easy swing and expansion.

Sliding doors

Sliding doors are generally made from thinner material because the full width of the door is supported. The thinner doors are also less bulky and permit more shelf space. However, for special purposes large sliding by-pass doors are made from thicker stock. They are generally suspended from the top on

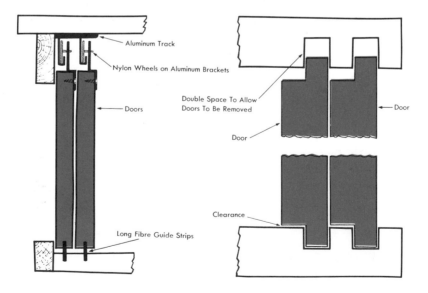

Fig. 29:11 ¾" By-pass Sliding Doors

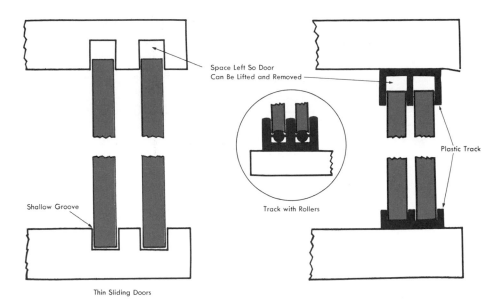

Space Left So Door
Can Be Lifted and Removed

Plastic Track

Shallow Groove

Track with Rollers

Thin Sliding Doors

Fig. 29:12 Sliding Door Guides and Track

hangers and rollers, as shown in Figure 29:11. Smaller doors are supported and guided at the bottom and the top either by grooves cut in the shelf or frame member, or by plastic or metal track. The track is usually sold as a set with the top track having grooves twice as deep as the bottom one. This allows the door to be easily lifted out of the cabinet at any time (see Figure 29:12).

Some tracks are equipped with rollers to make the doors slide more easily. Some of the materials used for thin sliding doors are ¼" plywood, wood-grained and plastic-covered hardboards, and glass.

Plywood edge treatment

Since plywood and composition boards are so extensively used in cabinet and furniture construction, several methods of concealing the exposed edges, which tend to be unattractive and hard to finish, have been devised. Some of these are shown in Figure 29:13.

Leg and rail joints

One of the more or less standard operations necessary in furniture construction is the joining of a table leg and a rail. Many otherwise good pieces of furniture are unstable because these two members have not been properly joined together.

The mortise-and-tenon is the old standby that is still the one most often used. However, there are several other good methods that make an attractive and secure joint between these two members. Some of them are shown in Figure 29:14.

To attach a table top

Table tops may be attached to legs, rails, or framing members by various means. The kind of fastening device will depend on the type of material used for the top. When solid stock is used, the off-set metal plate or wood block method should be used (see Figure 29:15, Diagrams A and B). This method per-

215

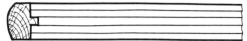

Solid Wood Glued to Edge

Self-Adhesive Wood Veneer

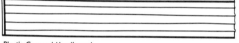

Solid Wood with a Tongue-and-Groove Joint

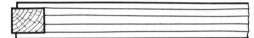

Wide Wood Strip

Plastic-Covered Hardboard

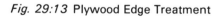

Wood Strip Set Between Face Veneer

Half-Round Moulding

Fig. 29:13 Plywood Edge Treatment

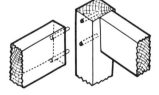

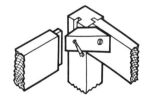

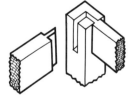

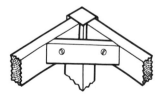

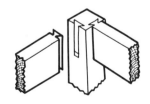

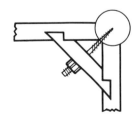

Fig. 29:14 Fastening Rail to Leg

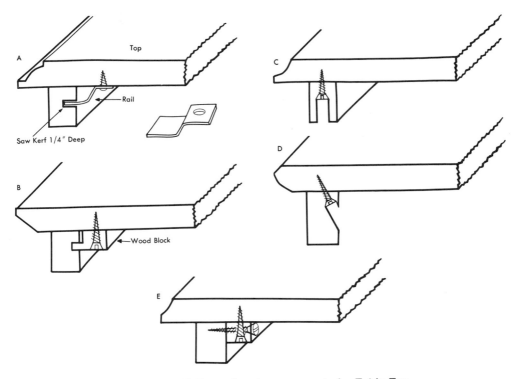

Fig. 29:15 Fastening Arrangements for Table Top

mits the top to shrink or swell without affecting the rest of the table. If the construction is of plywood or composition board, the shrinkage is negligible, thus allowing a more positive type of fastening to be used (Figure 29:15, Diagrams C, D, and E.) The use of any of these methods will enable the table to be disassembled for refinishing or shipping.

Turned legs

Where round turned legs are used on modern tables, they are usually fastened directly to the table top either by a wood joint or with special hardware. Although it is not difficult to attach the top without hardware, as shown in Figure 29:16, Diagram A, it is generally considered better practice to use the plates and screws shown in Diagram B. They are easily installed, make

a secure fastening arrangement, and have the added advantage that the legs can be removed at any time. Most plates are so made that the leg can be attached in a vertical position or at an angle.

Two ways of attaching rectangular legs to frames are shown in Figure 29:17.

Standard furniture dimensions

In the design of furniture and cabinets the variation in style, shape, over-all size, and design is almost limitless. However, certain standard dimensions have been established that suit the average human body. In the interest of comfort and serviceability careful consideration must be given to these sizes in the design and building of any furniture or cabinets. These dimensions need not restrict the design, as they

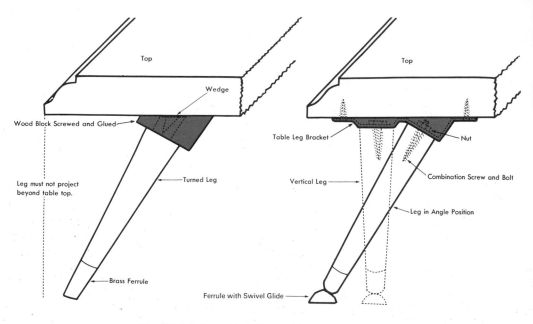

Fig. 29:16 Attaching Turned Legs to Table Top

can be adapted to any style of furniture. Some dimensions are critical, while others can vary. The height of a dining room table, for example, must be 29½" to 30", while the length and width of this table may vary to suit the design or purpose. Figures 29:18 and 29:19 illustrate some of the recommended dimensions in furniture design.

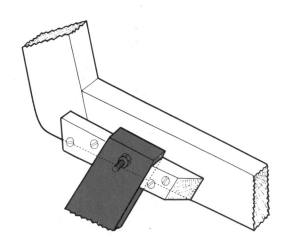

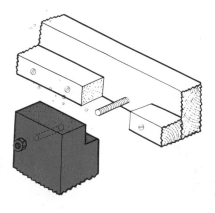

Fig. 29:17

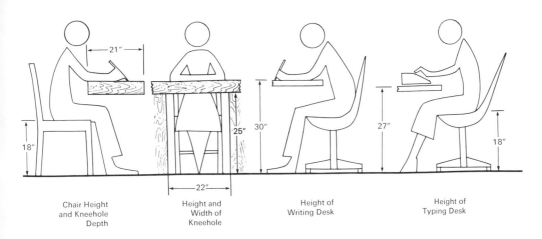

| Chair Height and Kneehole Depth | Height and Width of Kneehole | Height of Writing Desk | Height of Typing Desk |

Fig. 29:18 Standard Desk and Chair Dimensions

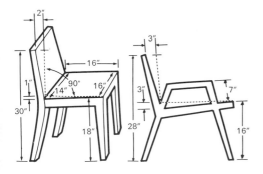

Fig. 29:19 Chair Dimensions

ASSIGNMENT

1. List some of the basic materials used in cabinet building.
2. What type of joint may be used between the gable and front frame?
3. List the two methods used for holding shelves in position.
4. How can the top of a cabinet be attached to the gables and front frame?
5. (a) List four types of frames used in cabinetmaking.
   (b) Describe any three types of these frames.
6. Name three wood joints used in drawer construction.

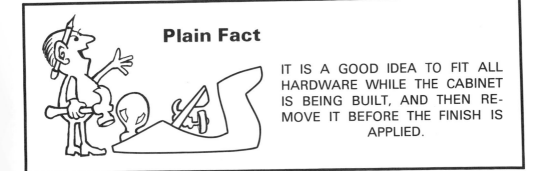

Plain Fact

IT IS A GOOD IDEA TO FIT ALL HARDWARE WHILE THE CABINET IS BEING BUILT, AND THEN REMOVE IT BEFORE THE FINISH IS APPLIED.

7. What clearance should be allowed for the width and depth of a drawer to make it slide freely without being too loose?

8. Describe three types of drawer slides.

9. Make a sketch of three types of cabinet door hinges.

10. (a) Describe three track arrangements in cabinets for sliding doors. (b) What materials are used for sliding doors?

11. By using sketches, show four methods of treating the edge of plywood.

12. What is the most common method of attaching table rails and legs? List two other methods.

13. (a) When a solid wood table top is to be used, how should it be attached to the rails?
(b) When the top is of plywood, what method of attachment can be used?

14. Describe the two methods of attaching round turned legs to a table top. Which method is considered better?

CHAPTER THIRTY

building materials

You will find it of interest and value to be familiar with some of the lumber and other building materials that are in general use throughout the country. We cannot hope to list all of the materials used in building construction and cabinetmaking, but the following are some in common use:

Dimensional stock

Square-edge dressed lumber that is sold in standard sizes such as 1"×6" or 1"×8" is called *dimensional stock*. The actual size of a 1"×6" is approximately ¾"×5¾".

Trim stock

Trim lumber, such as that used for door or window trim, is generally milled to some ornamental shape, as illustrated in Figure 30:1.

Moulding

Mouldings are made in a wide range of shapes and sizes. They are milled from top-quality stock and sold by the linear foot. Some of the mouldings are shown in Figure 30:2.

Siding

Figure 30:3 illustrates several types of exterior siding used on frame buildings. When calculating the quantity required, a percentage must be added

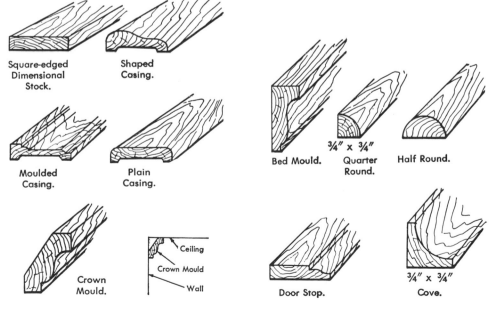

Square-edged Dimensional Stock.

Shaped Casing.

Moulded Casing.

Plain Casing.

Crown Mould.

Ceiling
Crown Mould
Wall

Bed Mould.

¾" x ¾"
Quarter Round.

Half Round.

Door Stop.

¾" x ¾"
Cove.

Fig. 30:1 Trim Stock

Fig. 30:2 Mouldings

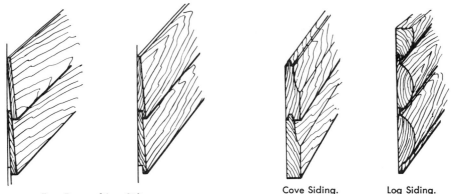

Two Types of Lap Siding.   Cove Siding.   Log Siding.

Fig. 30:3   Types of Sidings

because of the extra material required for lapping, matching, and waste.

Sheathing

Sheathing is the base lumber used under the shingles and siding of a house. The same material may be used under finished flooring and is called sub-flooring. Tongue-and-groove or other matched stock, as shown in Figure 30:4, is often used, although square-edge material is sometimes used for this purpose. Tongue-and-groove stock of a better quality is used for finished flooring.

Shingles

Roof shingles may be made of either wood or asphalt. Wooden shingles are available in various grades of cedar. Asphalt base shingles are manufactured by sprinkling a finely ground coloured crushed stone on an asphalt felt base. These shingles come in a wide range of colours, sizes, and types.

Shingles are sold by the *square*. A square of shingles consists of the number required to cover an area 10' × 10', or 100 square feet. Shingles are packed in bundles, the number of bundles to the square depending on the type.

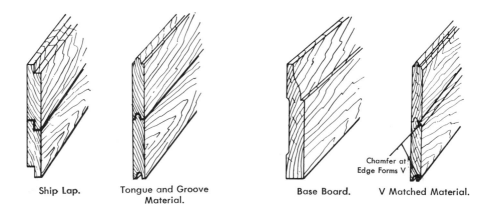

Ship Lap.   Tongue and Groove Material.   Base Board.   V Matched Material.

Chamfer at Edge Forms V

Fig. 30:4   *Fig. 30:5*

222

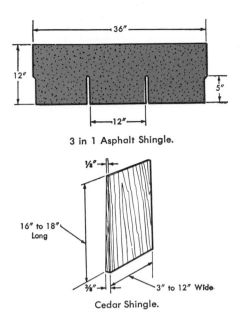

3 in 1 Asphalt Shingle.

Cedar Shingle.

Fig. 30:6

The quality of asphalt shingles is determined largely by their weight, with the 210 pounds per square being the weight of shingle most used.

Plywood

The strength of wood in proportion to its weight has been greatly increased in the form of plywood. This wood has a greater strength-weight ratio than steel. Plywood can be used quickly and easily, and has opened up a whole new field to the handyman as well as being of great assistance to the carpenter.

Plywood is made by laminating (gluing) three or more layers of veneer together. The layers are placed with the grain of each piece at right angles to that of the piece next to it. To reduce warping and to make a balanced construction, an odd number of layers is used, such as 3, 5, or 7. The number of plies of veneer used will depend on the thickness of the plywood, which varies from ¼" to 1". The standard width of the sheets is 48" and the lengths are 8', 10', and 12'.

Veneers have been used for many years in making furniture. One thin layer of expensive wood is laminated on the surface of a heavy, less expensive piece. It has, however, only been in the last few years that these thin layers of veneer have been glued to each other to make plywood as we now use it.

Veneer is cut from a log by placing it in a lathe arrangement, where it revolves against a long stationary knife that peels off long continuous sheets of veneer approximately ¹⁄₂₀" thick. Before they are turned, the logs are prepared by steaming them in large vats to make them soft and moist. The bark is then removed by spraying the log with water from high-pressure hoses. This is the rotary method of cutting veneer.

Veneer is also cut by slicing the thin sheets from a log that has been cut in the centre. The logs must be prepared in the same manner as for the rotary method. The sliced sheets of veneer are smaller, but a better figured or striped grain can be obtained. This type of veneer is often used for the face layer of the better plywoods.

There are many grades of plywood. *Sheathing grade* is unsanded and may have defects on both sides. It is made for roof and wall covering. Some plywoods are referred to as *G.1S.* (Good one side). This grade has one face that is sanded and has no defects. Other plywood is referred to as *G.2S.* (Good two sides), which means that either or both sides may be used as face sides. *Improved back* indicates that the defects have been removed or cut out and patches of sound wood have been inserted. Plywoods are now made with many decorative finishes for use as an interior wall finish.

The centre core of plywood is often thicker than the outside plies. This is done for economy and to make the ply-

223

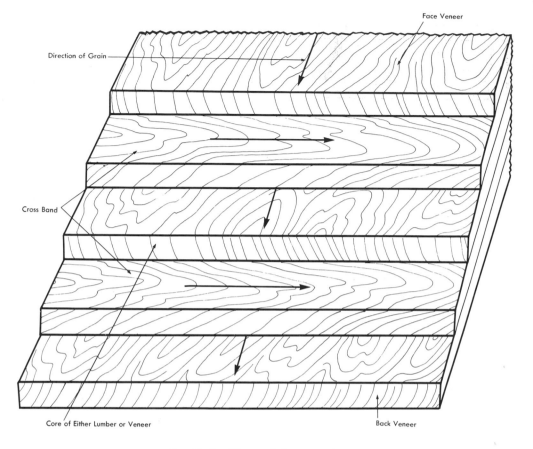

Face Veneer

Direction of Grain

Cross Band

Core of Either Lumber or Veneer

Back Veneer

Fig. 30:7   Plywood Construction

wood the desired thickness.

Plywood, as well as all types of wall-boards, is sold by the square foot. The price is determined by the thickness, the type, and the quality. Mouldings and trim stock are sold by the linear foot, often referred to as a *running foot*.

Hardboards

Hardboards are made by heating and compressing a mixture of wood fibre and adhesive. These boards are extensively used in woodwork. They are made in ⅛" and ¼" thickness, 4' wide, and from 4' to 10' long. You are probably familiar with *masonite*, which is

the trade name of one popular hard-board. It is also manufactured and sold by other companies under other trade names.

Hardboards are sold in either a *tempered grade*, which is very hard, or the *utility grade*, which is softer and less expensive. They are also made in the decorative peg-board type with equally spaced holes.

Fibre boards

Fibre boards also are made of wood or vegetable fibres, but they are not so tightly compressed. The porous nature of these boards gives them an ex-

224

cellent insulating quality. They vary in thickness from ⅜" to ¾" and are generally 4' wide, ranging in length from 8' to 10'. Fibre boards are extensively used for wall sheathing, plaster base, and for finished interior walls. Both hardboards and fibre boards are made in decorative, pre-finished colours or wood grains. A pre-finished material is one that has been painted, enamelled, stained, or printed before it is applied to a wall or ceiling. It requires no further finishing after it has been put in place. A combination fibre board and plywood is now made, where a hardwood sheet of veneer is glued to each side of a fibre board. The finished board is ¾" thick. This board warps less than plywood.

Gypsum boards

Gypsum boards are made with a layer of gypsum and lime between two surfaces of hard paper (see Figure 30:8). Gypsum board is made in sheets 4' wide and from 7' to 10' long in ⅜" to ½" thicknesses for interior wall finishes. It may also be used for exterior wall sheathing.

Both gypsum board and fibre board are extensively used for plaster base. However, when used for this purpose, they are made in smaller sheets, usually 16"×48", and are often referred to

as *lath*. Plaster base is the material that is nailed to the wall framework to form a base on which to apply the plaster.

Plastic-covered boards

Plastic-covered boards are now extensively used, both in furniture-making and in home construction. They are made in a great number of colours and designs, which are printed on paper attached to the face of a thin, fibre hardboard. Over this is placed a very thin layer of transparent plastic. Heat and pressure is applied to make a very hard, smooth, stainproof, shiny finish. *Arborite* is the trade name of one of these materials, which you may have seen or used. There are many others on the market.

In this book we have mentioned only the materials that are most often used in general woodworking. There are many others available, and others are still being developed.

Although wood as the basic raw material of the woodworker remains unchanged, the manufactured products made from wood and wood fibres are changing. New developments are constantly taking place in materials, machines, tools, and techniques.

The woodworking trade is not static but is constantly changing and growing to meet the needs of modern living. We believe you will find further study of woodwork interesting and rewarding.

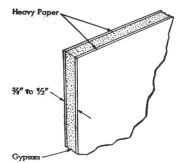

Heavy Paper

⅜" to ½"

Gypsum

Fig. 30:8 Gypsum Board

ASSIGNMENT

1. Draw the end view of one type of each of these materials: dimensional stock, trim stock, moulding, exterior siding, sheathing, subflooring.
2. Why is an odd number of layers of veneer used in the manufacture of plywood?

3. Why is the core layer of plywood sometimes thicker than the other plies?

4. Write a note on the two methods of cutting veneer.

5. Write out in full the meaning of *G.1S.*, *G.2S.*, and *Improved back*.

6. What would be the cost of 3 sheets of 4'×8' plywood at 28¢ per foot?

7. Explain the difference between hardboards and fibre boards.

8. At 8¢ per linear foot, what would be the cost of the crown mould required to go around a room 12'4" wide and 14'8" long?

9. What is meant by a *pre-finished surface* on a building material?

10. What is meant by "plaster base"?

11. How is gypsum board made? What is it used for?

12. How many squares of shingles would be required to cover a roof area 16'×32'?

13. Describe two materials used in general woodwork that have not been mentioned here.

14. Do you consider the study of woodwork and the practical experience of working with wood, tools, and machines to be of value to you in your education? If so, in what way?

glossary of terms

Abrasive – any rough material used for smoothing or grinding a surface.

Acetone – an organic solvent for plastic.

Adhesive – glue or glue-coated material.

Allen Screw – a short metal screw with a round head and a hexagonal slot.

Aluminum alloy – a material used for making machine parts that is light but strong. It is made by mixing aluminum with other metals to increase its strength.

Aluminum oxide – a compound of aluminum and oxygen.

American screw gauge – standard gauge for checking the diameters of wood screws.

Aniline dye – an oily liquid dye made from indigo or benzine and used in colouring wood stains.

Annual ring – a circular layer of wood produced yearly on the outside of the trunk of a tree beneath the bark.

Apprentice – a person in training for a trade.

Arbor – the shaft on which a circular saw blade is mounted.

Arc – any part of the circumference of a circle.

Arris – the line or edge at which two surfaces forming an exterior angle meet.

Band mill – a large band saw used in mills for sawing lumber from logs.

Bauxite – the clay-like, earthy mineral from which aluminum is made.

Bead – a rounded cut that generally runs the full length of a piece of stock.

Bed moulding – large decorative moulding often used around the eaves of houses.

Bench hook – a device that hooks over the edge of a bench and on which small work may be held.

Bench stop – a wood or metal peg that fits through a hole in a bench to act as a stop for work forced against it by the vise.

Benzine – a colourless, inflammable liquid made from coal tar, used as a solvent.

Bill of material – a list of the materials required for a specific job, stating their size, use, and type of wood.

Blank knives – shaper knives used as filler knives, or knives that have not been ground to shape.

Blemish – a mark or a stain that affects the appearance of a piece of wood.

Blued finish – a bluish, rust-resistant finish used on nails.

Brad – a finishing nail less than 1″ long.

Brad point – the point of a brad awl.

Building superintendent (construction) – the man in charge of the construction of a new building.

Burnisher – a long piece of hardened steel used for sharpening scrapers.

Butt hinge – a type of hinge used for hanging finished doors that is fastened to the edge of the door and the face of the door jamb.

Butterfly hinge – a type of ornamental hinge mounted on the face of a door.

Calibrated – marked off into graduations, such as fractions of an inch or degrees.

Cam – an elliptical-shaped bar or lever that changes regular circular motion into irregular circular motion or back-and-forth motion when it revolves.

Cambium layer – the layer of wood cells between the bark and the wood in which the growth of the bark and the wood takes place.

Carbide – a material manufactured from carbon that is harder than diamond and is used for cutting tools.

Casein glue – glue made from skim milk and chemicals.

Catalyst – a substance that starts or speeds up a chemical reaction in other substances when added to them, without undergoing any change itself.

Cellulose – a fibre that forms the chief part of the cell walls of plants and is much used as a base for plastics.

Chamfer – a groove or channel cut in a surface or a bevelled edge.

Chrome-plated – covered with a thin coating of chrome.

Chuck – a device for holding drills or bits or any other rotating tool or workpiece.

Clearance hole – a hole made large enough to accommodate the shank of a screw.

Closed-grain woods – woods with small wood cells (usually soft woods).

Coal tar dye – dye made from coal and used to colour wood stains.

Collar – a metal ring that fits over a shaft.

Compound angle – a double angle on a piece of stock, a cut made at an angle to the side and to the edge of a piece of stock.

Concave – curved inward like the interior of a circle or a hollow sphere.

Concealed hinge – a door hinge that is not visible when the door is closed.

Cone pulley – a pulley made with two or more steps of varying diameters.

Conifer – a tree, usually an evergreen, that bears cones.

Conservation – the conserving or saving of our natural resources.

Contact cement – an adhesive that when spread on two surfaces makes them stick together on contact.

Contour – the outline of a figure or a surface.

Convex – curved outward like the outside of a circle or a sphere.

Corrugated fastener – a wavy piece of metal used to secure two pieces of wood.

Countersink – a boring tool used to cut the recess for the head of a screw or bolt.

Crook warp – a bend in the edge of a piece of wood along the grain.

Cross-section – a section cut through the centre of an object at right angles to the axis.

Cup centre – a lathe centre made with a recessed centre section.

Cup warp – a cup-shaped bend in a piece of wood across the grain.

Cut nail – a square-shaped nail that has been stamped from sheet metal.

Cutter head – an attachment on saws and shapers used to hold the cutter knives.

Cutters – knives used on routers and shapers.

Cutting list – a list of materials to be cut for a project, specifying the rough sizes of each piece.

Dado cut – a groove cut across the grain of a piece of stock.

Dead centre – the lathe centre that does not revolve.

Deciduous trees – broad-leafed trees, generally hardwoods, that shed their leaves in the fall.

Diagonal – the distance between two opposite corners of a square or rectangular figure, or a line joining these two corners.

Dip-and-rub – a type of shellac finish.

Direct drive – the transmission of power through a direct connection of a machine, without the aid of pulleys or gears.

Door jamb – the sides of a door frame; the upright member to which a door is hinged.

Door pull – a door handle.

Door stop – a strip of wood on the door frame that stops the door from swinging through the opening.

Dowel – a cylindrical piece of stock used as a pin.

Dowelling jig – a device that makes easier the boring of dowel holes at right angles to the face of a joint.

Dressed lumber – lumber that has been planed.

Driers – ingredients used in paints to make them dry rapidly.

Dry rot – a wood decay caused by a lack of ventilation.

Dubbing – the slight rounding of a radius, a corner, or an arris.

Elliptical – having the form of an ellipse or an elongated circle.

Ethyl alcohol – alcohol made from grain, used as a solvent.

Expanding shield – a threaded metal tube that is inserted into a hole drilled in a masonry wall and into which a bolt is threaded, causing the shield to expand and tighten within the wall.

Exterior trim – the trim used on the exterior of houses.

Face nailing – nails driven in at right angles to the face of the work.

Face plate – a metal plate used on a lathe to turn such work as lamp bases and bowls.

Fasteners – holding devices such as nails, screws, and bolts.

Feather edge – the rough edge of a sawn board made feathery by the wood fibres, or a thin sharp edge that is easily broken or bent over.

Ferrule – a metal ring used on a chisel handle to prevent it from splitting.

Flint quartz – a natural stone used in the

manufacture of sandpaper.

Fluted bit – a bit with two grooves but no twist.

Flutes – grooves cut in wood or metal.

Forged – formed out of hot metal by hammering or stamping in a machine.

Fossil – any remains or traces of a plant or an animal of past geological ages found in the surface of the earth. Such material has become hard or fossilized through time.

French polish – a shellac-and-oil rubbed finish.

Friction catch – a spring-type door catch.

Galvanizing – a rust-resistant coating of zinc used on sheet metal and nails.

Garnet – a natural mineral used in the manufacture of sandpaper.

Gimlet – a form of drill used for making pilot holes for wood screws.

Gross – twelve dozen (144).

Gullet – the depression between two saw teeth.

Gypsum – a soft mineral used to make wallboard and plaster of Paris.

Habitat – the natural home of an animal or plant.

Hand screw – a hand clamp consisting of two jaws and two screws.

Hinge gain – the recess that is cut out of the door jamb and the edge of the door to receive the leaf of a butt hinge.

Hinge leaf – one of the two plates of a butt hinge.

Hinge pin – the pin that holds the two leaves of a hinge together.

Hold down – a spring device that holds the work firmly down on the table of a drill press or a shaper.

Hollow spindle – the main shaft of a lathe, made hollow so that the live centre can be removed from it.

Honing – the sharpening of a plane iron or a chisel on an oil-stone.

Hook angle – the angle of a hand-saw tooth, which is filed so that it is hooked or tilted toward the small end of the saw.

Idler wheel – a wheel on a shaft that acts as a stop or a guide for a blade or a belt.

Inlay work – strips or small pieces of wood set into a larger flat wood surface.

Interior trim – finishing lumber used on the interior of a house.

Japan drier – a drying agent used in paints and varnishes.

Jig – a device used in production to accurately position pieces of wood or metal for drilling or cutting.

Journeyman – one who has completed his trade apprenticeship.

Keeper plate – the metal plate attached to a door jamb that receives the bolt from the lock and thus keeps the door closed.

Kerf – the cut made by a hand saw or a power saw.

Kick-back fingers – the short metal strips on a circular saw guard that prevent the work from kicking back toward the operator.

Kiln – a large, oven-like arrangement used to dry or season lumber.

Lac insects – the insects that secrete the resinous substance "lac", used in making natural shellac and varnishes.

Laminate – to glue thin layers of material together.

Lateral – sideways.

Lathe rod – a rod inserted through the hollow spindle to remove the live centre on a wood lathe.

Linear measurement – measurement along a straight line.

Magnetic catch – a cupboard door catch that has a magnet on one side and an iron or steel plate on the other.

Matched lumber – tongue-and-groove lumber.

Medulla – pith, the soft material in the very centre of a tree.

Medullary rays – rows of wood cells running out from the centre of the tree toward the bark.

Methyl acohol – commercial wood alcohol.

Mill – retail lumber yard where lumber is sold and machine woodwork is done. (*See also* Sawmill.)

Mineral spirits – commercial turpentine.

Moisture meter – a device used to measure the moisture content of wood.

Molecule – the smallest particle of an element that can exist and still have the properties of the substance.

Morse taper – a standard taper used in fitting metal parts together.

Mortise – a recess cut in a piece of work to receive a tenon.

Mortising attachment – an attachment used

on the drill press for cutting mortises.

Mould – in pattern-making, the form or receptacle made by placing damp sand around a wooden pattern, used for the making of metal castings.

Mouldings – strips of wood cut into ornamental shapes.

Naphtha – a type of fuel made from petroleum or coal tar and often used as a solvent.

Neoprene – a type of plastic used for grips on tool handles.

N.G.R. stains – non-grain-raising, commercial wood stains.

Nitric acid – an inorganic acid, used in the production of nitrated cotton, the basis of lacquers.

Offset screwdriver – a screwdriver with the handle at a right angle to the driving point.

Oil stain – wood stain with a linseed oil base.

One-piece cutter – a solid cutter head used on a shaper.

Open-faced knives – individual flat knives used on a shaper.

Organic acid – a weak acid found in nature that contains carbon and hydrogen, called organic because of its origin.

Organic compound – any chemical compound made up of carbon and hydrogen (hydrocarbon), a substance originating from things living or that once were living.

Paraffin – a by-product of petroleum used to make wax.

Paring – cutting with a chisel.

Peg-board – a masonite-type fibre board with equally spaced holes bored in it.

Penny size – standard term used to denote the sizes of nails.

Perpendicular – straight up and down, plumb.

Phillips head screws – screws with a star or X-shaped slot.

Pigments – small particles of coloured matter used in paints and stains.

Pilot hole – a starting hole for wood screws.

Pitch pockets – cavities filled with pitch that occur in wood.

Pivot action – swinging or teetering from a central point.

Plank – a lumber term for a piece of stock 2″ to 4″ in thickness and 8″ and over in width.

Plaster base – a wood, fibre, or gypsum material used as a base for plaster.

Ploughed cut – a groove parallel with the grain.

Plumb – in a vertical position.

Polygon – a many-sided, closed figure with straight sides. Regular polygons have all sides and angles equal.

Primer – a base or sealer coat of paint.

Protractor – an instrument for measuring degrees, or laying out angles.

Pumice stone – finely ground rock powder used as an abrasive.

Pythagorean Theorem – In a right-angle triangle the square on the hypotenuse is equal to the sum of the squares on the other two sides.

Quarter-sawn – a method of sawing lumber from a log so that the annual rings are approximately at right angles to the surface of the board.

Rabbet cut – a groove cut parallel to the grain, out of the edge of a piece of stock.

Ratchet – a device used on wrenches and screwdrivers that allows the handle to turn without the head being moved.

Reactive monomer – a compound with simple molecules or single units that are able to react (combine) with other compounds.

Recessed – set into or set below the surface.

Resin (natural) – organic substances secreted by most plants and used in making glue and varnish.

Resin (synthetic) – a man-made plastic compound that is the main ingredient of such materials as celluloid and bakelite.

Resin glue – glue made with a synthetic resin base.

Rim speed – the speed of the outside diameter of a wheel or pulley.

Robertson head screws – wood screws with a square or socket-type slot.

Rosin – a gum obtained from fossils and pine trees and used in the manufacture of varnish.

Rottenstone – a very finely ground rock powder used as an abrasive for rubbing down or polishing a finish.

Routing – the cutting of grooves, rabbets, dadoes, or inlay channels.

Sabre blade – a stiff blade used on the jigsaw with only one end of the blade attached to the machine.

Sash – the part of a window that contains the glass.

Sawmill – an establishment where logs are

cut into lumber by machines.

Screw set – a tool used for making a starting hole for a screw when attaching hardware.

Scribed line – a line cut, drawn, or scored.

Sealer – a material that is spread over a porous surface before painting.

Semi-concealed hinge – a hinge that is only partly visible.

Serrated – having notches or teeth cut or pressed into the surface.

Set screw – a small threaded screw used to fasten one metal part to another, e.g. a pulley to a shaft.

Shearing cut – a cut made at an angle to the grain of the wood.

Shellac – a transparent finishing material made by dissolving purified lac in alcohol.

Silex powder – a finely ground, white quartz powder used as a base for paste wood filler.

Silicon carbide – an extremely hard crystalline compound made from sand and carbon, used as an abrasive.

Silicon powder – an abrasive made from sand.

Skotch fasteners – a staple-type fastener used on butt joints.

Slip stone – a cone-shaped carborundum stone used for sharpening gouges.

Soluble – able to be dissolved or liquefied by another material.

Solvent – a substance that will dissolve another substance.

Specifications – a detailed description of the materials to be used for a given job, stating sizes, grades, and type.

Spindle turning – turning on a wood lathe with the work held between centres.

Spiral nail – a nail with a twisted or thread-like shape.

Spirit level – a tool used for levelling or plumbing. It contains glass tubes with alcohol and air bubbles.

Spirit stain – an alcohol-base wood stain.

Spirits – alcohol.

Splitter block – the solid part of a circular saw guard that passes through the saw cut.

Sprocket – a flat wheel with teeth on the circumference that fit into the open links of a chain.

Static – fixed or stationary.

Stop chamfer – a chamfer that does not ex-

tend the full length of the piece of stock.

Stove bolt – a term used to describe small metal bolts.

Straightedge – a piece of metal, wood, or plastic used for testing surfaces or drawing straight lines.

Sub-assemblies – two or more parts that are attached together to form a part of a completed project.

Surface catch – a door catch mounted on the surface of a door.

Surface hinges – hinges mounted on the surface of the work: e.g. T-hinges, butterfly hinges, and strap hinges.

Swing saw – a circular saw and motor that is mounted on an overhead arm, allowing the saw to swing down to the work.

Tang – the pointed end of a chisel that fits into the handle; the tapered part of the shank of a bit that fits into a bit brace.

Template – a pattern.

Tenon – a tongue projecting from the end of a piece of wood, cut to fit into a recess in another piece of wood to form a mortise-and-tenon joint.

Termites – insects that bore holes in wood.

T hinge – a surface hinge made in the shape of a T.

Timber – a term given to standing trees, cut logs, or stock that is 5″ and over in thickness and 5″ and over in width.

Toggle bolt – a bolt with a swing arm attached to one end, used for bolting hardware to a lath-and-plaster hollow wall.

Tool steel – a good-quality steel used in the manufacture of cutting tools.

Torque – the force created by a rotating shaft.

Tungsten carbide – an extremely hard substance made from tungsten and carbon.

Urea formaldehyde – a crystalline substance used in the manufacture of synthetic resin glues.

Vat – a large container used to hold liquid.

Veining – cutting a series of fine grooves.

Veneers – very thin layers of wood that have been peeled or sliced from a log.

Wane – the bark-covered or imperfect edge of the sawn board formed by the surface of the log.

Warp – the curvature of a piece of wood in thickness, width, or length due to shrinkage or swelling.

Wet rot – a decay in wood caused from exposure to moisture.

Whetting – sharpening the edge of a chisel or plane iron on an oil-stone.

White lead – a white paste used as a pigment for paint and as the base for putty.

Wind – the twist in a board (propeller shape).

Wind sticks – two parallel sticks used for testing the wind in a piece of stock.

Working face – the face side of the stock.

Zinc oxide – a compound of zinc and oxygen used in the manufacture of paint.

bibliography

Advanced Woodwork and Furniture Making, by John L. Feirer (Charles A. Bennett Company Inc., 1971)

Basic Woodworking Processes, by H. Hjorth and E. W. Fowler (Bruce Publishing Company, 1961)

Cabinetmaking and Building Construction, by Edward Harris (McGraw-Hill, 1967)

Cabinetmaking and Millwork, by Alf Dahl and J. Douglas Wilson (American Technical Society)

Canadian Woods: Their Properties and Use, Information Canada, Ottawa

Carpentry in the Home Workshop, by Clarence Herisko (Collier Books, 1963)

Complete Book of Wood Finishing, by Robert Scharff (McGraw-Hill, 1956)

The Complete Woodworking Handbook, by Jeanette Adams and Emanuela Stieri (Arco Publishing Co., Inc.)

Constructive Design, by B. N. Osburn (Bruce Publishing Company, 1948)

Contemporary Furniture Making for Everybody, by John G. Shea (Van Nostrand Reinhold Company, 1965)

Designs in Wood, by Paul Bridge and Austin Crossland (B. T. Batsford Ltd.)

Easy Ways to Expert Woodworking, by Robert Scharff (McGraw-Hill, 1956)

Fundamentals of Woodturning, by Archie S. Milton and Otto Kwahlers (Bruce Publishing Company)

Furniture You Can Build, A Sunset Book (Lane Book Company, 1966)

General Woodworking, by Chris H. Groneman (McGraw-Hill, 1965)

General Woodworking, by William H. Johnson and Louis V. Newkirk (Collier-Macmillan Ltd., 1946)

How To Build Modern Furniture, 2nd edition by Mario Dal Fabbro (McGraw-Hill, 1957)

Introducing Furniture Making, by John R. Trussel (B.T. Batsford Ltd., 1970)

Machine Woodworking, by R. E. Smith (McKnight & McKnight Publishing Co., 1958)

Modern Woodworking: Tools, Materials and Procedures, by Willis H. Wagner (The Goodheart-Willcox Company, Inc., 1967)

Native Trees of Canada, Information Canada, Ottawa

Principles of Woodworking, by H. Hjorth and William F. Holtrop (Bruce Publishing Company, 1961)

Steel Square, 2nd edition, by Gilbert Townsend (American Technical Society, 1947)

The Use of Hand Tools and Portable Machinery, Delmar Publishers, Inc.

Wood Finishing – Plain and Decorative, by F. N. Vanderwalker (Drake Publishers, Ltd., 1970)

Wood Laminating, by J. Hugh Capron (McKnight & McKnight Publishing Co., 1963)

Woodworking Fundamentals, by William D. Wolansky (McGraw-Hill, 1962)

index

239

27 37 47 57 67 77 87 97 08 RF 9 8 7 6 5 4 3 2 1

CANADIAN HARDWOODS

Birch   Red Oak   Elm

Beech   Walnut   Ash